THE LATERAL LOGICIAN

THE LATERAL LOGICIAN

LATERAL THINKING PUZZLERS

CHALLENGING LATERAL THINKING PUZZLES

GREAT LATERAL THINKING PUZZLES

by Paul Sloane and Des MacHale

Illustrated by Myron Miller

Quality Paperback Book Club
New York

The Lateral Logician

LATERAL THINKING PUZZLERS

by Paul Sloane

ACKNOWLEDGMENTS

The author acknowledges the inspiration of Martin Gardner, Edward de Bono, Bruno Brookes, and Gyles Brandreth. The puzzle 'The Two Writers' is an idea created by D. StP. Barnard and was originally published in the *Daily Telegraph* in 1978. "The Dream" is the copyright of Times Newspapers and was first published in the *Sunday Times* in 1990.

Edited by Claire Wilson

CONTENTS

Dedicated to Jackie, Katy and Hannah without whose help and inspiration this book would not have been possible.

INTRODUCTION

This book is the result of the many years I spent collecting lateral thinking problems and the happy hours I whiled away trying to figure them out. The reader will doubtless find that some of the puzzles are familiar old faithfuls, but I guarantee that he or she will also find some interesting new ones.

Edward de Bono first coined the phrase "lateral thinking" to refer to a process of thinking that is different from the normal linear, or forward thinking to which we are accustomed. In traditional reasoning, we progress logically from one step to the next. However, in lateral thinking, you must deliberately abandon this process in order to eliminate inhibitions. You then try to solve problems in different, random, or lateral ways.

Most of the problems in this book take the form of situations that at first seem unlikely or illogical. The idea is to work out the set of circumstances that describes the situation. The first section consists of the puzzles, which are split into four categories according to their approximate level of difficulty and a special historical section. The second section consists of leads and clues to give intermediate help with each puzzle. Finally, the last section contains the answers.

Although the reader can work through the book on his or her own, it is much more fun to treat the puzzles as challenges for small groups, either as an after-dinner game or as a lateral thinking exercise. For these events, the best course of action is for one person to act as the quizmaster. He or she, knowing the answer, would then give the question to the group. The leader can then answer questions from the players in one of three ways—yes, no, or irrelevant. The task of the group is to completely solve the problem as fast as it can. This can prove a stimulating, infuriating, and ultimately enjoyable exercise!

If the group gets stuck, then the quizmaster can help by giving some of the leads or clues in the help section.

In asking questions about a situation, you should first test all assumptions. Then make broad attacks on the problem before homing in on promising lines of enquiry. Above all, you should try to think laterally, that is to cast away conventional approaches and to make leaps of the imagination.

THE PUZZLERS

1 Easy Puzzlers

1.1   The Man in the Elevator

For a start, here's one of the oldest and best-known lateral thinking problems. It goes like this:

A man lives on the tenth floor of a building. Every day, he takes the elevator to the first floor to go to work or to go shopping. When he returns, he always takes the elevator to the seventh floor and then walks the remaining flights of stairs to his apartment on the tenth floor. Why does he do this?

1.2   Bombs Away!

One night during the Second World War, an allied bomber was on a mission over Germany. The plane was in perfect condition and everything on it worked properly. When it had reached its target, the pilot ordered the bomb doors opened. They opened. He then ordered the bombs released. They were released. But the bombs did not fall from the plane. Why should this be so?

1.3   The Coal, Carrot, and Scarf

Five pieces of coal, a carrot, and a scarf are lying on the lawn. Nobody put them on the lawn, but there is a perfectly logical reason for their being there. What is it?

1.4   The Two Americans

There were two Americans waiting at the entrance to the British Museum. One of them was the father of the other one's son. How could this be so?

1.5   The Man Who Hanged Himself

Not far from Madrid, there is a large wooden barn. The barn is completely empty except for a dead man hanging from the central rafter. The rope around his neck is ten feet long and his feet are three feet off the ground. The nearest wall is 20 feet away. It is not possible to climb up the walls or along the rafters, yet he hanged himself. How did he manage it?

1.6 The Men in the Hotel

Mr. Smith and Mr. Jones are two businessmen who book
into the same hotel for the night. They are given adjacent
rooms on the third floor. During the night, Mr. Smith
sleeps soundly. However, despite being very tired, Mr.
Jones cannot fall asleep. He eventually phones Mr. Smith
and falls asleep immediately after hanging up. Why
should this be so?

1.7 The Silent Cabbie

A London cab driver picked up a lady who was a notorious chatterbox. He did not want to engage in conversa-

tion, so he pretended to be deaf and dumb. He pointed to his mouth and ears to indicate that he could neither speak nor hear. After she alighted, he pointed to the meter so that she could see how much she owed. She paid him and walked off. Then she realized that he could not have been a deaf mute. How did she know?

1.8   A Peculiar House

Mrs. Jones wanted a new house. She very much liked to see the sun shining into a room, so she instructed the builders to construct a house of which all four walls face south. After much thought, the builder managed to erect just such a house. How did he do it?

1.9   Death in the Phone Booth

A man is lying dead in a telephone booth. The telephone handset is swinging. Two of the windows are broken. He was not murdered. How did he die?

1.10   The Man in the House

A man entered a house. There was no one else in the house. He walked into a room, stopped, and then slowly raised his hands above his head. After a moment, he turned around, let out a laugh, and left. Why?

1.11   A Chess Piece

Two grandmasters played five games of chess. Each won the same number of games and lost the same number of games. There were no draws in any of the games. How could this be so?

1.12   Happy or Sad

Three women dressed in swimsuits were standing together. Two were sad and one was happy. But the sad women were both smiling and the happy one was crying. Why should that be so?

1.13   The Unseen Walker

On a busy Friday afternoon, a man walked several miles across London from Westminister to Knightsbridge without seeing anybody or being seen by anybody. The day was clear and bright. He had perfect eyesight and he looked where he was going. He did not travel by any method of transport other than by foot. London was thronged with people yet not one of them saw him. How?

1.14   The Dream

The boss of a storage warehouse had just arrived at work when one of his employees burst into his office. The man explained that while asleep the previous night he had dreamed that one of the stored boxes contained a bomb that would explode at two p.m., causing a terrible fire. The boss was skeptical, but agreed to investigate. After a search, a bomb was found in the area foreseen in the man's dream. The police were called, the bomb defused, and a tragedy averted. Afterwards, the boss thanked the employee sincerely and then fired him.

The sacked man had not planted the bomb, and his prophetic dream had saved the warehouse from destruction. Yet the manager was right to fire him. How could that be so?

1.15   In the Pet Shop

A pet shop was advertising puppies for sale. Two men entered the shop. The first put ten dollars on the counter and asked for a puppy. The assistant asked whether he would prefer a poodle, a Labrador, or an Alsatian. He chose the poodle. The second man also put ten dollars on the counter and asked for a puppy. The assistant did not utter a word. He simply gave the man an Alsatian puppy. How did he know that this was what the man wanted?

1.16 The Coffee Drinker
. . . .
A man in a restaurant complained to the waiter that there was a fly in his cup of coffee. The waiter took the cup away and promised to bring a fresh cup of coffee. He returned a few moments later. The man tasted the coffee and complained that this was his original cup of coffee with the fly removed. He was correct, but how did he know?

1.17 One Step Beyond
. . . .
A man stood looking through the window on the sixth floor of an office building. Suddenly, he was overcome by an impulse. He opened the window and leapt through it. It was a sheer drop outside the building to the ground. He

12

did not use a parachute or land in water or on any special soft surface. Yet the man was completely unhurt when he landed. How could that be so?

1.18 The Turkish Bath Mystery

Four men met every Thursday lunchtime at the Turkish Baths. Joe, a musician, always brought his personal cassette player so that he could listen to music. Jack, a banker, brought a thermos containing a drink. Jim and John were both lawyers and brought paperback books to read.

One day in the mist-filled room, John was found dead from a deep wound through his heart. The police were called immediately. They questioned all three suspects, but no one said that they had seen anything happen. A thorough search was carried out, but no murder weapon could be found. What happened?

2 Moderate Puzzlers

2.1 Anthony and Cleopatra

Anthony and Cleopatra are lying dead on the floor in an Egyptian villa. Nearby is a broken bowl. There are no marks on their bodies and they were not poisoned. Not a person was in the villa when they died. How did they die?

2.2 Five Men

Five men were proceeding together down a country path. It began to rain. Four of the men quickened their step and began to walk faster. The fifth man made no effort to move any faster. However, he remained dry and the other four got wet. They all arrived at their destination together. How could this be so?

N.B. They relied only on foot power!

2.3　Trouble with Sons I
A woman had two sons who were born in the same hour of the same day in the same year, but they were not twins. How could this be so?

2.4　Trouble with Sons II
A woman sat at her kitchen table with her two sons. She spoke to each of her sons and they replied to her, but the sons never spoke to each other. The boys had not fallen out and did not dislike each other. Although they conversed freely with their mother, they never addressed a word to one another. Why?

2.5 The Two Sisters

One day, two sisters decided to clean out the old shed at the bottom of their garden. When they had finished the cleaning, one of them had a dirty face and the other had a clean face. The sister with the clean face went and washed her face, but the girl with the dirty face did not wash. Why should this be so?

2.6 The Miller's Daughter

Many years ago, there was a poor miller who could not afford to pay the rent on his mill. His grasping old landlord threatened to evict him, his wife, and his daughter. However, the landlord did offer an option. If the miller's beautiful young daughter would marry the old man, then he would forget their debts and let the miller and his wife live in the mill rent-free.

The family met to discuss this proposition. The daughter was horrified at the prospect of marriage to the old man, but she realized that it might be the only hope for her parents. She suggested a compromise. They would draw lots. If the landlord won, she would meet his request and if she won, he would wipe out all debts without her having to marry him. The landlord agreed.

The two stood on a stony path that had many black and white pebbles. The landlord suggested that they put one black pebble and one white one in a bag. She would have to draw a pebble from the bag. If it were black, she must marry him and if it were white she would be free. She reluctantly agreed to this suggestion. He bent down and picked up two pebbles to put in the bag, but she noticed that he had cheated and put in two black pebbles.

She could expose him by showing that there were now two black pebbles in the bag, but he would lose so much face in front of all the people there that he would be very angry and probably evict them. How could she seem to go along with the plan and triumph knowing that there were two black pebbles in the bag?

15

2.7 Water and Wine

There are two glasses on the table, one containing water and the other one wine. They both contain exactly the same amount by volume. If you take a teaspoon of water and mix it into the wine and then take a teaspoonful from the wine glass and mix it with the water, both glasses become contaminated. But which is the more contaminated? Does the water now contain more wine than the wine does water or the other way round?

2.8 The Man in the Painting

A man stands in front of a painting and says the following: "Brothers and sisters have I none. But this man's father is my father's son." How is the man in the painting related to the man who is in front of it?

2.9 The Single Statement

An explorer was captured by a tribe whose chief decided that the man should die. The chief was a very logical man and gave the explorer a choice. The explorer was to make a single statement. If it was true, he would be thrown over a high cliff. If it was false, he would be eaten by lions.

What statement did the clever explorer make that forced the chief to let him go?

2.10 Birthday Blues

The day before yesterday Freda was 17. Next year she will be 20. How can this be so?

2.11 The Four Sheep

Farmer Giles has four sheep. One day, he notices that they are standing in such a way that they are all the same distance away from each other. That is to say, the distance between any two of the four sheep is the same. How can this be so?

2.12 A Geography Question

A ship passed through the Panama Canal from west to east. That is to say, it entered the west end of the Canal and left at the east end. However, immediately after it left the canal, it entered the Pacific Ocean. It did not double back through the canal, nor did it sail backward. How could this be so?

2.13 Family Reunion

At a family reunion, it was found that the following relationships existed between the people present: Father, Mother, Son, Daughter, Uncle, Aunt, Brother, Sister, Cousin, Nephew, Niece. However, there were only four people there. How could this be so?

2.14 Crossing the Desert

Two trucks have to carry the same heavy loads across a desert. One is an older truck with an older driver, Joe, who knows his way to the village that is their destination. The other truck is more modern, but its driver, Jim, does not know the way. They agree that the modern truck will follow the older one. Unfortunately, Jim has forgotten to fill up with fuel. By the time he does this, the first truck is well out of sight. However, it has left very clear tracks in the sand, and Jim follows them.

After some time, the tracks start to become less and less clear. Eventually, they disappear altogether. This surprises Jim, because there is no wind to cover the tracks and his own tracks are still very clear. There is no sign of the other truck, but in due course a bedouin on a camel arrives, and, with his help, Jim gets to the village. There, he meets Joe and discovers the reason why the tracks disappeared. What was it?

2.15 Old Mrs. Jackson

Mr. and Mrs. Jones were young and active people. Their next-door neighbor, Mrs. Jackson, was a 93-year-old invalid. One day, they asked her into their house to do something that neither of them could do. There was no skill that she had that one of them did not have, so why did they need her help?

2.16 Matrimonial Problems

John and David were brothers. John married Jane. David married Diana. The strange thing was, John and Diana shared the same wedding anniversary. David's wedding anniversary was one month before this date and Jane's was one month after it. None of them had ever divorced or remarried. What was going on?

18

2.17 The Man with the Wood

A man had some wood. On Monday, it was in the shape of a cube. On Tuesday, he changed it into the shape of a cylinder, and on Wednesday, he changed it into the shape of a pyramid. He did not cut or carve the wood into these shapes. How did he do it?

2.18 Stuck Tight

A truck became wedged under a low bridge. It could not move forward or back without severely damaging its roof. The truck driver was perplexed until a little girl standing nearby suggested an easy solution. What was it?

2.19 Coming Home

A man walked home after having been out drinking. He walked down the middle of a deserted country road. There were no street lights to illuminate the road and there was no moonlight. He was dressed all in black. Suddenly a car that did not have its headlights on came racing down the road. At the last moment, the driver of the car saw the man and swerved to avoid him. How did he manage to see him?

2.20 A Riddle

For a little light relief, we will now have an old riddle. What is it that gets wetter as it dries?

2.21 Another Riddle

What is it that the man who makes it does not need; the man who buys it does not use himself, and the person who uses it does so without knowing?

2.22 The Horse Dyed

A man went buffalo hunting. He rode a beautiful white stallion and carried a powerful rifle to shoot his prey. Unfortunately, the buffalo could see the white horse approaching and ran off long before he could shoot. The hunter hit on the plan of dying the horse brown so as to camouflage it. He painted a brown dye on the horse and went hunting again. The camouflage worked, but he was even less successful with his hunting than before. Why?

2.23 Push That Car

A man pushing his car stopped outside a hotel. As soon as he got there, he knew he was bankrupt. Why?

2.24 The Unrequested Kiss

In the middle of the day, a young woman approached a man in the street. Without either of them saying a word,

she gave him a long kiss on the lips. She had never seen him before and she did not know who he was. She did not find him attractive and she was not rewarded for her actions. So why did she kiss him?

2.25   The Two Golfers
. . . .
Archie and Ben were professional golfers and keen rivals. One day during a game, they had each scored 30 when Ben hit a bad shot. Archie immediately added 10 to his own score. Archie then hit a good shot and he had won the game. Why?

3 Historical Puzzlers

3.1 Sew What?

In 1685, it was decided that a portrait should be painted of the Duke of Monmouth. However, a needle and thread were required before the artist could begin his work. There was nothing wrong with the Duke's clothes, so why were the needle and thread needed?

3.2 The Grateful Prisoner

In 1902 in the French West Indies Mr. Cyparis was in prison awaiting trial for drunkenness. He was detained longer than he expected, was neglected, and was left without food and water. Yet when he was released, he was grateful to have been in prison. Why should that be so?

3.3 Ben Jonson

Ben Jonson was a great English poet and playwright who lived from 1572 until 1637. Why was he buried in a sitting position?

3.4 Lord Strathallen

Lord Strathallen was an important Scottish nobleman who was used to getting what he wanted. One day in 1746, he ordered some food and drink even though he was neither hungry nor thirsty. What he wanted was not available and he was offered whiskey and oatcake instead. He was glad to quickly consume a little of each. Why?

3.5 A Remarkable Journey

In 1930, two men drove from New York to Los Angeles in a Ford motor car. The journey of 3,340 miles took 18 days.

This wasn't the first, the fastest, or the slowest journey

of its kind. They drove on normal roads. The car was not remarkable and the two men were normal. But because of this journey, these two men hold a world record that endures to this day. What is it?

3.6 The Two Writers

George and Evelyn never met but they carried on writing until late in life. It has been said that Evelyn loved George, but she was in any event too old for him. George married in 1880. He converted to Catholicism in 1930. During World War II, he served with the Royal Marines and the Royal Horse Guards. Partly in recognition of this, Evelyn's subsequent writings analyzed the character of World War II and the struggle between good and evil.

Evelyn died in 1966 near Taunton in Somerset. She had achieved notoriety for her unconventional views and life-style. Her first full-length novel had been published in 1859. She is buried in Highgate Cemetery. He died at the age of 62 having published his autobiography in 1964. He lived one year longer than she did. How could this be so?

3.7   World War I

At the beginning of the first World War, the uniform of the British soldiers included a brown cloth cap. They were not provided with metal helmets.

As the war went on, the army authorities and the War Office became alarmed at the high proportion of men suf-fering head injuries. They therefore decided to replace the cloth headgear with metal helmets. From then on, all sol-diers wore the metal helmets. However, the War Office was amazed to discover that the incidence of head injuries then increased. It can be assumed that the intensity of fighting was the same before and after this change. So why should the recorded number of head injuries per bat-talion increase when men wore metal helmets rather than cloth caps?

3.8   King George IV

King George IV was born in 1763. He was king of England from 1820 until his death in 1830. He was not a great king, but he did start a new trend in footwear. His boots were different from everybody else's. The innovation concern-ing his boots was copied and it is commonplace today, but at the time was very unusual. What was it?

3.9   Walk This Way

Johann Hurlinger, an Austrian, set a world record by walk-ing the 871 miles from Vienna to Paris in 55 days. He averaged only 1.5 miles per hour and he did it in 1900, yet the record stands today. What is so special about it?

4 Difficult Puzzlers

4.1 Death in a Field

A man is lying dead in a field. Next to him is an unopened package. There is no other creature in the field. How did he die?

4.2 Death in Rome

Mr. Jones is reading his daily newspaper. He reads an article with the following headline: "Woman dies in holiday accident." It goes on to say, "Mrs. Rigby-Brown, while on holiday with her husband in Rome, fell to her death from the balcony of her seventh-floor room."

Mr. Jones turns to his wife and says "That was not an accident. It was murder." He had never met either of the Rigby-Browns, so how could he know it was murder?

4.3 Woman on the Bridge I

During the second World War, there was a footbridge over a ravine between Germany and Switzerland. It was guarded by a German sentry. His orders were to shoot anyone trying to escape over the bridge and to turn back anyone who did not have a signed authorization to cross. The sentry was on the German side of the bridge. He sat in a sentry post and he came out every three minutes to survey the bridge.

There was a woman who desperately needed to escape from Germany to Switzerland. She could not possibly get a pass. She knew that she could sneak past the sentry while he was in the sentry post, but it would take between five and six minutes to cross the bridge. There was no place to hide on or under the bridge, so the guard would be easily able to shoot her if he saw her on the bridge escaping to Switzerland. How did she escape across that bridge?

4.4 Woman on the Bridge II

In South America, a woman was being chased by a gang of bandits. She had escaped with two solid gold balls, and the bandits wanted to kill her and take the balls. She came to a wooden bridge over a deep ravine. The bridge was 100 feet long. There was a notice on the bridge that said "Maximum weight on this bridge 112 pounds." Strangely enough, this notice was 100% accurate—the bridge would break if it carried more than 112 pounds. She weighed 100 pounds and each of the two balls weighed 10 pounds. There was no time to leave one ball behind and come back for it later. And yet she managed to escape across the bridge to safety with both the balls. How could this be so?

4.5   Trouble with Sons, Again!

This is more of a probability teaser than a lateral thinking problem, but it can prove amusing.

Mrs. Jones has two children. At least one is a boy. What are the chances that both are boys?

Mrs. Brown has two children. The younger is a boy. What are the chances that both are boys?

4.6   Silence on the Train

A man boarded a train and sat in a carriage. The only other person in the carriage was a woman who was sitting opposite him. After a little while, she took from her bag a pencil and paper and passed it to the man. He wrote on the piece of paper and gave it back to her. At the next stop, she got off the train and threw the piece of paper away.

They had never met before. Their meeting on the train was by chance and not arranged. They did not speak to each other.

Can you determine the story behind this sequence of events?

4.7   The Lonely Man

A man lived alone in a house for two months. Nobody came to visit him and he never went out. At the end of that time, he became deranged. One night he put out the fire, turned off the lights, and walked out of the house. He was never seen or heard of again. His actions in leaving that house resulted in the deaths of 90 people. Why was that?

4.8   The Distant Image

A man was in a room. It was ten feet square and ten feet high with solid walls, ceiling, and floor. There were no windows and the door was close fitting and closed. It was a dark night and no light entered the room from outside.

There was a light on in the room. Apart from the light, there was no other electrical or powered object in the room. The interesting thing is this—although the room was only ten feet across, the man could see something 40 feet away. How could that be?

4.9   Coins of the Realm

Why are 1988 pennies worth more than 1983 pennies?

4.10   Baby Has Lots

What is it that a baby has more of than an adult?

4.11   The Hotel Detective

A hotel detective was walking along the corridor of a large hotel one day. Suddenly, he heard a woman's voice cry out "For God's sake, don't shoot me John!" Then there was a shot. He ran to the room from where the shot came and burst in. In one corner of the room, lay a woman who had been shot through the heart. In the middle of the floor was the gun that had been used to shoot her. On the other side of the room stood a postman, a lawyer, and an accountant. The detective looked at them for a moment and then went up to the postman, grabbed him, and said "I am arresting you for the murder of that woman."

It was, in fact, the postman who had murdered the woman, but how did the hotel detective know? Never before had he seen any of the people in the room.

4.12   Faster Than the Speed of Sound

What was the first man-made object to travel faster than the speed of sound?

The speed of sound is about 1100 feet per second (340 metres per second). Concorde travels faster than the speed of sound. But the answer to this question is an object created a long time before Concorde.

4.13 Concorde

A businessman had an important business meeting that led him to fly by Concorde from London to New York.

When he left home in the morning, his wife drove him to the airport and accompanied him to the check-in. She then waved good-bye as he went through to Passport Control and the Departure Lounge. She did some shopping at the airport shops and returned to the car at which time she saw the Concorde take off on time.

His flight on Concorde from London to New York was of course a direct flight. When he reached New York, he went directly through Immigration and Customs. He had no baggage to collect as he only took a briefcase for his short trip. He went through to the arrivals hall and there waiting to greet him was his wife! It was only that morning that she had seen him off. She had not flown nor taken a boat so how could she be there to meet him?

4.14 Asphyxiation

A woman was found gassed in her bedroom. The gas fireplace had been left on. The windows and door were locked from the inside. She had been seen entering the room by her sister. It looked to the police as though she had accidentally put the gas on and forgotten to light it, so they put it down as an accident. In fact, her husband had murdered her. How?

4.15 The Slow Mover

Although the people who come to see it think it moves forward, it actually moves backwards. It started about seven miles from where it is today and is moving now much slower than in the past. Previously, it travelled as much as five feet a year, but now it's travelling less than half that distance. Despite its slow speed, most of the people who have tried to ride along on it have perished in the attempt. What is it?

4.16 Dinner for Three

An ancient Arabic puzzle goes like this: A hunter met two shepherds, one of whom had three loaves and the other, five loaves. All the loaves were the same size. The three men agreed to share the eight loaves equally between them. After they had eaten, the hunter gave the shepherds eight bronze coins as payment for his meal. How should the two shepherds fairly divide this money?

4.17 A Theological Puzzle

Years ago, a boy was brought before his headmaster because he had not learned his scripture lesson. After a long lecture, the headmaster offered to let him off his beating if he could show that he knew anything about God that the headmaster did not know. The boy then asked a question that completely stumped the man: "What is it that you can see and I can see but that God can never see?"

The headmaster thought there could be no answer, but when he heard the boy's response, he had to concede that it was true. So the clever boy escaped his punishment. What was the answer?

4.18 It's a Knock-out!

A policeman was called because a man was found lying unconscious outside a shop. As soon as the man came around, he was arrested. He was not a known criminal and had not been engaged in any kind of fight or dispute before losing consciousness. Why did the policeman arrest him?

4.19 The Frustrated Policemen

The police in Venezuela have been trying to arrest a notorious criminal for some time. They know where he lives. On several occasions, they have obtained a warrant for his arrest and have gone to his house. However, as soon as they enter the house, he locks himself in his bedroom. The police then go away frustrated. Why should that be so?

4.20 Neighbors

Ali, Ben, and Cyril were born in 1309, 1310 and 1311 in the same district in old Jerusalem. They grew up and lived their whole lives in this same area. Each lived to be over 60 and each had a full and active life. However, the three men never saw each other. Why should that be so?

4.21 The Fatal Fare

A man got into a taxi and told the driver his destination. After that, they did not say a word. On the way, the taxi driver stopped the taxi at a lonely spot and beckoned the man to get out. The driver then picked up a stone and dealt his passenger a heavy blow to the head, killing him. He then drove off.

The taxi driver was not a criminal. He had never met the passenger before nor did he recognize his face or voice. He did not rob the man. Why did he kill him?

4.22 One Clock

In the days before watches were invented, clocks were valuable items. There was a man who had one clock in his house. It kept good time, but one day he found that it had stopped. He had no idea what the correct time was. He walked to the next valley to visit his friend who had a clock showing the right time. He spent a little while chatting with his friend then he walked home. He did not know the exact length of the journey before he started. How did he manage to set his one clock correctly on his return?

5 Fiendish Puzzlers

5.1 The Man in the Bar I

For its brevity, its simplicity, and its difficulty, this problem has some claims to be the best lateral thinking problem ever.

A man walked into a bar and asked the barman for a glass of water. They had never met before. The barman pulled a gun from under the counter and pointed it at the man. The man said 'Thank-you' and walked out. Why should that be so?

5.2 The Man in the Bar II

A man walked into a bar and asked for a drink. The man behind the bar pulled out a gun and shot the man. Why should that be so?

5.3 The Man in the Bar III

A man who wanted a drink walked into a bar. Before he could say a word, he was knocked unconscious. Why?

5.4 Another Man in a Bar

Two brothers were having a drink in a bar. Suddenly, one of the brothers got into a heated argument with the barman. He pulled a knife and, despite his brother's attempts to stop him, stabbed the barman in the chest.

At his trial, he was found guilty of assault with a deadly weapon and grievous bodily harm. At the end of the trial, the judge said "You have been found guilty of a vicious crime. However, I have no choice but to set you free."

Why should this be so?

5.5   The Deadly Block of Wood

A man lies dead inside a trailer. He has shot himself. Close by him is a block of wood. It is a plain piece of wood about two feet long by one inch wide (61cm by 2cm). The wood carries no writing or other markings and yet, it is fair to say that the sight of this piece of wood on this day caused the man to commit suicide. Why should this be so?

5.6   The Two Barbers

A traveller came to a small town. He had never visited it before, he knew no one there, and he knew nothing about the town or its inhabitants.

He needed a haircut. There happened to be two barber shops close to each other on the main thoroughfare—the only barber shops in town. The man studied each of them with care. One shop was very neat and tidy. Everything about it was smart. The barber was sweeping away the last traces of hair from the floor while waiting for his next customer.

The other barber's shop was very untidy. Everything looked rather run down and ramshackle. The scruffy-looking barber within was lolling on a chair waiting for his next customer.

Both shops charged the same amount for a haircut. After careful consideration, the traveller decided to go to the scruffy barber for his haircut. Why?

5.7   The Mongolian Postal Service.

The Mongolian Postal Service has a strict rule stating that items sent through the post must not be more than 1 metre long. Longer items must be sent by private carriers, and they are notorious for their expense, inefficiency, and high rate of loss of goods.

Boris was desperate to send his valuable and ancient flute safely through the post. Unfortunately, it was 1.4 metres long and could not be disassembled as it was one long, hollow piece of ebony. Eventually, he hit on a way to send it through the Mongolian Postal Service. What did Boris do?

5.8   Heaven

A man died and went to Heaven. There were thousands of other people there. They were all naked and everyone looked as they did at the age of 21.

He looked around to see if there was anyone he recognized. Suddenly, he saw a couple, and he knew that they were Adam and Eve. How did he know?

5.9   Fool's Gold

You must choose between two cylinders. They are identical in size and appearance. Each is painted green. However, one is solid and made of a non-magnetic alloy. The other is hollow and made of gold. They both have solid ends. They both weigh the same, measure the same, and have the same density. You are not allowed to scratch through the paint. How can you simply tell which cylinder is made of gold?

5.10   The Man in the Bar, Again!

A man walked into a bar and asked for a drink. The barman had never met the man before but without saying a word he pulled out a gun and shot him dead. Why?

5.11 The Plane Hijacker

A few years ago in the USA, a young man hijacked a passenger flight at gunpoint. He ordered the pilot to fly to a different airport and radioed his demands to the airport authorities. In return for the safe release of the plane and hostages, he asked for 100,000 dollars in a bag and two parachutes. When the plane landed, he was given the bag of money and the two parachutes. He then instructed the pilot to take off again and to fly at a fairly low altitude towards their original destination. When they were over a deserted part of the country, he strapped on one of the parachutes and, clutching the bag of money, leapt from the plane. The second parachute was not used.

He was never found. The task of the police is to find that hijacker. Your task is different. You have to answer one question. Why did he ask for two parachutes if we assume that he only ever intended to use one?

5.12 Wealth Tax

The governing body of the state of Lateralia was extremely concerned about the uneven distribution of wealth in the country. They thought it unfair that the richest man in the country should have so very much more than his poorer compatriots. They therefore instituted a wealth tax decreeing that each year the wealthiest man in the country had to give away his money by doubling the wealth of every other citizen, starting with the poorest and working up to the second wealthiest person if possible. This decree was carried out, and the richest man gave away his money by doubling the wealth of all other citizens. However, the governing body was shocked to find that this action had made no difference to the overall distribution of wealth nor to the relative wealth of the poorest and richest citizens. How could this be so?

5.13 Death on the Train

A man stepped out of a speeding train to his death. He had been on his own in the compartment, and all that was found there was a very large handkerchief. If he had made the journey by any means other than train, he would almost certainly not have decided to commit suicide. Why did he take his life?

5.14 The Amorous Commuter

John Jones lives in Maidenhead. He has one girlfriend in Reading and another in Slough. He has no car and therefore takes the train whenever he goes to see them.

Trains stopping in Maidenhead can go either east or west. If they are westbound they will go to Reading. If they are eastbound, they will go to Slough. There are an equal number of trains going in each direction.

John likes his two girlfriends equally. Because he finds it hard to choose between them, he decides that when he goes to the station, he will take the first arriving train, regardless of whether it is going east or west. After he has done this for a month, he finds that he has visited the girl in Slough 11 times as often as he visited the girl in Reading. Assuming that he arrived at Maidenhead station at random times, why should the poor girl in Reading have received so little of his attention?

5.15 Short Roads

There are four main towns in Lateralia. We will call them A, B, C and D. They lie at the corners of a ten-mile square. In order to improve communications between the towns, the Lateralian Department of Transport decided to build a new road linking all four towns together. Because they had very little money, it was decided that the new road system should be as short as possible and still allow access from any one town to any other. The engineers came up with the three designs shown below. Number one uses 40 miles of road, number two uses 30 miles of road, and number three uses 28.3 miles of road. The designers naturally recommended plan number three because it employed the smallest road area and, therefore, cost the least. However, when they submitted their plan to the Minister of Finance, he accused them of extravagance and quickly pointed out a better design that required even less total road surface. What was his superior solution?

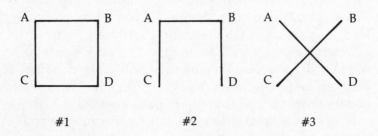

#1   #2   #3

5.16   The Hunter and the Bear

There is a well-known puzzle that goes like this:

There was a hunter who started out from his camp one morning. He walked one mile due south and then saw a bear. He followed it eastward for exactly one mile, at which point he shot it. He then dragged it northward for one mile to the same camp that he had started from. What color was the bear?

5.17   The Arm of the Postal Service

One day a man received a parcel in the post. Inside, he found a human left arm. He examined it carefully and then repacked it and sent it on to another man. The second man also examined the arm. He then took it out to the woods and buried it. Why should they have done these things?

5.18   A Weighty Problem I

A shopkeeper wants to be able to dispense sugar in whole pounds ranging from one pound up to 40 pounds. He has a standard, equal-arm balance weigh scale. Being of an extremely economical outlook, he wants to use the least possible number of weights to enable him to weigh any number of pounds between 1 and 40. How many weights does he need and what are they?

5.19   A Weighty Problem II

This problem is more than weighty, it is devilish.

You have an equal-arm balance scale and twelve solid balls. You are told that one of the balls has a different weight from all the others, but you do not know whether it is lighter or heavier. You can weigh the balls against each other in the scale balance. Can you find the odd ball and tell if it is lighter or heavier in only three weighings?

THE CLUES

1 Easy Puzzlers

1.1 The Man in the Elevator

Q: Is there anything that he does between the seventh and tenth floors other than climb stairs?
A: No.

Q: If he had someone else with him, would they both get out at the seventh floor and walk up to the tenth floor?
A: No.

Q: If he lived on the sixth floor, would he go up to the sixth floor in the elevator?
A: Yes.

Q: If he lived in a different block of apartments in a different country but still on the 10th floor, would he still get out on the 7th floor when going up?
A: Most probably yes.

1.2 Bombs Away!

Q: Would the fact that the bombs did not fall surprise any of the crew?
A: No.

Q: If that same plane was parked on the runway and the bomb doors were opened and the bombs released, would they fall?
A: Yes.

Q: Was the manner in which the plane was flying the cause of the bombs not dropping?
A: Yes.

1.3 The Coal, Carrot, and Scarf

Q: Does the time of year matter?
A: Yes.

Q: Were the coal, carrot, and scarf brought out to the garden by human beings?
A: Yes.

Q: Were they used for some entertainment purpose?
A: Yes.

1.4 The Two Americans

This one is based on a familiar theme. You either get it quickly or not at all. It does not lend itself to a long line of intelligent questioning. It boils down to the simple question—how can two people have the same son?

1.5 The Man Who Hanged Himself

Q: Was there anybody else involved before, during, or after his suicide?
A: No.

Q: Did he stand on something in order to reach the rafter?
A: Yes.

Q: Has that something now gone?
A: Yes.

Q: Did someone take it away?
A: No.

1.6 The Men in the Hotel

Q: Was there something happening in Mr. Smith's room that was preventing Mr. Jones from sleeping?
A: Yes.

Q: Was it a noise?
A: Yes.

Q: Did they speak for long on the phone?
A: No.

1.7 The Silent Cabbie

This little problem is best solved by thinking clearly about how a passenger uses a taxi. What communications take place between passenger and cabbie?

1.8 A Peculiar House

This house had only four walls and they all faced south. Think about the shape of the house, then think about where it might be located.

1.9 Death in the Phone Booth

Q: Was he talking to someone when he died?
A: Yes.

Q: Was his death an accident?
A: Yes.

Q: Did anything external hit the phone booth?
A: No.

Q:Did he break the phone booth windows?
A: Yes.

Clue: There was a fishing rod outside the phone booth.

1.10 The Man in the House

Q: Was he frightened when he raised his hands?
A: Yes.

Q: Was it his house?
A: No.

Q: Had he heard a sound that made him raise his hands?
A: Yes.

Q: Did he laugh because he was surprised and relieved?
A: Yes.

1.11 A Chess Piece

This is the kind of problem that depends on the reader or listener making the wrong initial assumptions. Test all the assumptions with questions like the following:

Q: Were they playing normal chess?
A: Yes.

Q: In chess, if one player wins then the other loses?
A: Yes, always.

Q: So when one grandmaster won a game, the other grandmaster lost it?
A: No.

Q: Was there anybody else involved?
A: Yes.

1.12 Happy or Sad

Q: Were they on the beach or at a swimming pool?
A: No.

Q: Is it relevant that they were wearing swimsuits?
A: Yes.

Q: Were they beautiful, shapely women?
A: Yes.

Q: Was the happy one crying because she was happy?
A: Yes.

Q: Were the sad ones smiling because they were sad?
A: No.

1.13 The Unseen Walker

Q: If he walked into this room now, would we see him and he see us?
A: Yes.

Q: Did he wear anything special?
A: Yes. *Clue:* It was a miner's helmet.

Q: Did he walk along normal roads?
A: No.

1.14 The Dream

Q: Was the man sacked because he had had anything to do with planting the bomb?
A: No.

Q: Had the man genuinely dreamed about the bomb?
A: Yes.

Q: Did the boss have a grudge of some kind against the man?
A: No.

Q: Were the man's particular responsibilities relevant?
A: Yes.

44

1.15 In the Pet Shop

Q: Was this the last puppy?
A: No, there were plenty of puppies of all three breeds.

Q: Were any of the three men known to each other.
A: No.

Q: Did the second man gesture in any way that he wanted the Alsatian?
A: No.

Q: Had the customer ever been in the shop before?
A: No.
Clue: Every dog has his price.

1.16 The Coffee Drinker

Q: Was there something about the cup itself that identified it?
A: No.

Q: Was the fly still in the cup?
A: No.

Q: Could the man have known it was the same cup if he had not tasted it?
A: No.

1.17 One Step Beyond

Q: Was he holding a rope?
A: No.

Q: Did he have special powers or could anyone have done this?
A: Anyone could have done this.

Q: Did he fall from six floors and land on the ground outside the building?
A: No.

Q: Did he jump through the window?
A: Yes.

1.18 The Turkish Bath Mystery

Q: Was John murdered by one of his three companions?
A: Yes.

Q: Was he stabbed by one of them?
A: Yes.

Q: Did the murderer bring the weapon into the baths with him?
A: Yes.

Q: Could the police have found the weapon if they had searched harder?
A: No.

2 Moderate Puzzlers

2.1 Anthony and Cleopatra

This is an old one. It can prove a little difficult if you have not heard it before.

The most fruitful lines of questioning are those that try to establish the exact cause and circumstances of death. To cut a long story short, it can be said that their deaths followed the accidental breaking of the bowl. The bowl had contained water. They died from lack of oxygen.

2.2 Five Men

Q: Did the man who stayed dry carry any kind of umbrella or other covering?
A: No.

Q: Did he walk?
A: No.

2.3 Trouble with Sons I

This is one of those problems that can appear totally mystifying and impossible to explain. However, you will kick yourself when you hear the answer.

Suffice it to say that the two boys are brothers, born of the same mother and father on the same day of the same year at the same place. But they were not twins. What else could they be?

2.4 Trouble with Sons II

Q: Were all three people physically normal with full faculties of speech, hearing, sight, etc.?
A: Yes.

Q: Had they ever spoken directly to each other?
A: No.

Q: Would they like to speak to each other?
A: Yes.

Q: Is there any physical barrier that prevents them conversing?
A: No.

Q: Had they grown up together?
A: No.

2.5 The Two Sisters

This is another problem that involves making the wrong assumptions. In this case, you need to question the assumptions and motivations of the two girls.

Q: Did the girl who washed want to clean her face?
A: Yes.

Q: Did she think that her face was dirty?
A: Yes.

Q: So the girl who did not wash thought that her face was already clean?
A: Yes.

2.6 The Miller's Daughter

You have to think of a way whereby she could use the fact that she knows she will draw a black pebble to give a result that will indicate a white pebble. If that is too obscure just remember that a double negative is a positive, that should help.

2.7 Water and Wine

This is quite a celebrated little problem. It can be solved mathematically or by the application of some common sense and lateral thinking.

The important point to bear in mind is that, after the two transfers, each glass contains the same volume that it started with and the same volume as the other glass.

2.8 The Man in the Painting

This is a simple little riddle but it often causes consternation. If you get into a muddle with it then just divide the sentence into three parts:

Brothers and Sisters have I none,
But this man's father
Is my Father's Son.

Now work backwards from the last statement.

2.9 The Single Statement

The explorer must make a statement that is both true and false at the same time. Better still, it should be a statement that means that any action the chief takes would place him in the position of having acted illogically.

Can you construct a statement about the way the explorer will die that is neither true nor false?

2.10 Birthday Blues

Freda has to have three birthdays between the day before yesterday and the end of next year. So the birthday has to fall around the turn of the year. You should be able to get it from there.

2.11 The Four Sheep

Start by defining how three sheep can be equidistant from each other—it's easy isn't it?

Your mind should then jump from a triangle to a square. But if you find that a square cannot produce a solution then, you need to start thinking laterally, i.e. along different lines entirely!

2.12 A Geography Question

Q: Did the ship enter the canal from the Caribbean Sea?
A: Yes.

Q: It then sailed from the west end of the canal to the east end?
A: Yes.

Q: And it then entered the Pacific Ocean?
A: Yes.

Q: Was this a special ship in some way?
A: No.

Q: Does every ship do this?
A: Yes.

2.13 Family Reunion

This is not a trick question in any sense. All the relationships are present between the people there. Do not start with any false assumptions. For example, husband and wife are not mentioned!

Try leaving the brother and sister relationship to last and start with the aunt, uncle, cousin, etc.

2.14 Crossing the Desert

This is a conventional lateral thinking problem with a familiar underlying theme. Concentrate the questions on why the tracks of the old vehicle (only) should grow gradually fainter and disappear.

2.15 Old Mrs. Jackson

Q: Did Mrs. Jackson perform any physical action for the Joneses?
A: Yes.

Q: Was it something that they could do or learn to do for themselves?
A: No.

Q: Would Mrs. Jackson have been able to perform the same service for some other couple?
A: Yes.

2.16 Matrimonial Problems

Each sentence in itself is true. The key is the second sentence. These questions should help make things a little clearer:

Q: Is John married to Jane?
A: No.

Q: Is David married to Diana?
A: No.

Q: Is John married to Diana?
A: Yes.

Q: Is David married to Jane?
A: No.

2.17 The Man with the Wood

Q: Did he have it in blocks that he rearranged?
A: No.

Q: Did he use fire or heat to mould it?
A: No.

Q: Was it wood from a tree?
A: Yes.

Q: Did changing the wood's shape require a special skill?
A: No.

2.18 Stuck Tight

Q: Were the bridge and truck normal?
A: Yes.

Q: Could the road be lowered or the bridge raised?
A: No.

Q: Was the girl's idea easy to implement, without any special equipment?
A: Yes.

2.19 Coming Home

Q: Was the man carrying a torch or any other illumination?
A: No.

Q: Was there any starlight or lightning?
A: No.

Q: Did the driver see the man?
A: Yes.

Q: Could anyone have seen him?
A: Yes.

2.20 A Riddle

It is difficult to give any clues on this neat riddle other than to advise you to consider the question actively, not passively!

2.21 Another Riddle

It could also be said that nobody wants it, but everybody needs it!

2.22 The Horse Dyed

Q: Did the brown dye make the horse slower or less able to chase buffalo?
A: No.

Q: Was it solely the dye that caused the deterioration in his hunting chances or was there some other factor (such as fewer buffalo or worse light)?
A: It was solely the dye.

Q: Did the dye make the horse harder to see?
A: Yes.

2.23 Push That Car

Q: Did he have to push the car?
A: Yes.

Q: Could the car ever be driven?
A: No.

Q: Was the hotel on a famous road?
A: Yes.

Q: Was he bankrupt because he had to pay money to the hotel owner?
A: Yes.

2.24 The Unrequested Kiss

Q: Did she expect to kiss someone on this day?
A: No.

Q: Was there a rational reason for her behaviour?
A: Yes.

Q: Was he expecting a kiss?
A: No.

Q: Was there anything unusual about him?
A: Yes.

Q: Did she do it to help him?
A: Yes.

2.25 The Two Golfers

Clues should not be needed on this one as you have all the information you require to work out the answer, even if you know nothing about golf or its scoring!

3 Historical Puzzlers

3.1 Sew What?

Q: Were the needle and thread needed for the canvas?
A: No.

Q: Was the artist a normal portrait artist?
A: Yes.

Q: Was there something wrong with the Duke of Monmouth?
A: Yes.

Q: Was he alive?
A: No.

3.2 The Grateful Prisoner

Q: Did he meet someone or learn something in prison?
A: No.

Q: Was he better off when he left prison than when he entered it?
A: No.

Q: Was he cured of some disease or illness?
A: No.

Q: Is his offense relevant?
A: No.

Q: Did he enjoy being in prison?
A: No.

Q: Did he avoid something by being in prison?
A: Yes.

3.3 Ben Jonson

Q: Had he asked to be buried in a sitting position?
A: No.

Q: Was it usual for people to be buried like that?
A: No. Extremely unusual.

Q: Did it have something to do with his profession?
A: Yes.

Q: Was he buried in a normal church graveyard?
A: No.

3.4 Lord Strathallen

Q: Did he need the food and drink for some medical condition?
A: No.

Q: Did the whiskey and oatcake meet a real need that he had?
A: Yes.

Q: What did he ask for?
A: Wine and bread.

Q: Was his request urgent?
A: Yes.

3.5 A Remarkable Journey

An important point in the description is that they hold a world record. It is not just a record for going from New York to Los Angeles. The distance and manner of their journey are what count.

It is a remarkable record. It does not involve silly aspects of the car or the men. If in doubt, think laterally!

3.6 The Two Writers

This is really a literary quiz disguised as a lateral thinking problem. If you need some clues then try the following.

George wrote *Silas Marner*. Evelyn wrote *Brideshead Revisited* in 1945, some 86 years after she had written *Adam Bede*.

3.7 World War I

Q: Did the men wear the helmets?
A: Yes.

Q: When they wore the helmets, did the incidence of head injuries increase?
A: Yes.

Q: And yet helmets were retained?

A: Yes.

Q: Were they beneficial?
A: Yes.

3.8 King George IV

What was new about King George IV's footwear had nothing to do with buckles, laces, tongues, heels, soles, color, or material. It was much more fundamental.

3.9 Walk This Way

Q: Did he walk unaided all the way?
A: Yes.

Q: Was he physically handicapped or abnormal in any way?
A: No.

Q: Would it be an easy record to beat?
A: No.

Q: Did he walk on stilts or on any special footwear, or did he carry anything?
A: No.

Q: Were his feet very sore when he finished?
A: No.

4 Difficult Puzzlers

4.1 Death in a Field

Q: Was his death an accident?
A: Yes.

Q: Did he die in the field, in the spot where he lies?
A: Yes.

Q: Was anyone else present in or around the field at the time?
A: No.

Q: If he had been able to open the packet would that have saved him?
A: Yes.

Q: Did he know he was going to die as he entered the field?
A: Yes.

4.2 Death in Rome

Q: Had Mr. Jones ever met either of the Rigby-Browns?
A: No.

Q: Was he right in saying it was murder?
A: Yes.

Q: Was Mr. Rigby-Brown the murderer?
A: Yes.

Q: Had Mr. Jones ever communicated in any way with
Mrs. Rigby-Brown?
A: No.

Q: Had Mr. Jones, in his professional capacity, provided
some service to Mr. Rigby-Brown?
A: Yes.

Q: Did he deduce from this service and the newspaper
article that Mrs. Rigby-Brown had been murdered?
A: Yes.

4.3 Woman on the Bridge I

Q: Did she escape by running over the bridge or hiding on
it?
A: No.

Q: Did she escape by tricking the guard in some way?
A: Yes.

Q: Did the guard follow his orders?
A: Yes.

4.4 Woman on the Bridge II

Q: Did she roll the balls over the bridge?
A: No.

Q: Did she throw them to the other side?
A: No.

Q: Did she take them with her as she crossed the bridge?
A: Yes.

Q: Yet the weight on the bridge never exceeded 112
pounds?
A: Correct.

Q: Did she use some special skill?
A: Yes.

58

4.5 Trouble with Sons, Again!

The answers to the two questions are, of course, different. Try writing down all the possible combinations of boys and girls that can constitute two children. Then work out which of these combinations are applicable in the cases of Mrs. Jones and Mrs. Brown.

4.6 Silence on the Train

This requires some thorough questioning. Here are some useful questions and one or two clues:

Q: Did they recognize each other in any way?
A: No.

Q: Did the man make any movements or gestures?
A: Yes. *Clue:* with his mouth.

Q: Was the man remarkable in any way?
A: Yes. *Clue:* he was a famous author.

Q: Was the woman remarkable in any way?
A: Yes. *Clue:* she was deaf and mute.

4.7 The Lonely Man

Q: Is what he did after leaving the house relevant?
A: No.

Q: Could he have left the house earlier?
A: Yes.

Q: Was it an ordinary sort of a house?
A: No.

Q: Did he perform some function or duty within the house?
A: Yes.

Q: Was the cessation of this function or duty the cause of the deaths of the 90 people?
A: Yes.

Q: Were they involved in some form of travel when they died?
A: Yes.

4.8 The Distant Image

Q: Was there anything else in the room other than the man and the light?
A: Yes.

Q: Were the other thing(s) in the room necessary to the sighting of something 40 feet away?
A: Yes.

Q: Did this man have special skills or powers?
A: No.

Q: Would anyone there have been able to see the thing 40 feet away?

A: Yes.

4.9 Coins of the Realm

Q: Are the 1988 pennies in better condition than the 1983 pennies?
A: No.

Q: Are the 1988 coins rarer than the 1983 coins?
A: No.

Q: Were pennies minted in 1988 and 1983?
A: Yes (but irrelevant!).

4.10 Baby Has Lots

Q: Is the answer something abstract, such as innocence or expectations?
A: No. The answer is something physical that a baby has more of than an adult.

Q: Does the number that a baby has reduce as he or she gets older?
A: Yes.

Q: Does everybody have them and need them?
A: Yes.

Q: Are they part of the body?
A: Yes.

Clue: A baby has about 350 of them and an adult about 206.

4.11 The Hotel Detective

Q: Was the profession of each of the three suspects immediately apparent?
A: No.

Q: Was each wearing normal working clothes?
A: Yes.

Q: Were they wearing name badges or other identifiers?
A: No.

Q: Was it something to do with the position or use of the gun?
A: No.

Q: Was it a brilliant or difficult piece of detective work?
A: No.

Q: Would it have been obvious to most people who the murderer was?
A: Yes.

4.12 Faster Than the Speed of Sound

Q: Does this object make a loud noise as it breaks the speed barrier?
A: Yes.

Q: Is it in use today?
A: Yes.

Q: Is it possible for a man to throw something faster than the speed of sound?
A: No.

Q: Was it normally used as a weapon?
A: No.

Q: Is it easy to get it to break the sound barrier or does it require great strength or skill?
A: Fairly easy for most adults.

4.13 Concorde

This is another problem that repays the questioning of all assumptions made.

Q: Did his wife travel (other than from home to the airport and back again)?
A: No.

Q: Was she in New York to meet him?
A: Yes.

Q: Was she in London to see him off?
A: No.

Q: Did someone else see him off from London?
A: No.

4.14 Asphyxiation

Q: Did anyone other than the woman enter the room?
A: No.

Q: Did she die from breathing gas?
A: Yes.

Q: Had she lit the oven?
A: Yes.

Q: Was the oven faulty in any way?
A: No.

4.15 The Slow Mover

Q: Is it a living thing?
A: No.

Q: Are there many examples of this type of phenomenon?
A: Yes.

Q: Do people come to see it because it is a spectacular sight?
A: Yes.

4.16 Dinner for Three

This is a very straightforward puzzle with no tricks or catches. However, the right answer is not three coins to the shepherd who had three loaves and five coins to the shepherd who had five loaves. That would not be fair!

4.17 A Theological Puzzle

For the purposes of this problem, it is assumed that there is only one God and that God is the supreme being, all knowing and all seeing.

4.18 It's a Knock-out!

Q: Did he suffer from some medical condition or physical disability?
A: No.

Q: Did someone else knock him out?
A: No.

Q: Was he knocked out by a blow to the head?
A: Yes.

Q: Was there anything lying near him?
A: Yes. *Clue:* It was a brick.

4.19 The Frustrated Policemen

Q: Could they arrest him if he stayed in the kitchen or hallway?
A: Yes.

Q: Could they arrest him if his bedroom door was unlocked?
A: No.

Q: Could they arrest him in the street?
A: Yes.

Q: Is the layout of the house the important factor?
A: Yes.

Q: Is there something that physically prevents people from entering his bedroom?
A: No.

4.20 Neighbors

Q: Was there some physical barrier that kept them apart?
A: No.

Q: Were they blind?
A: No.

Q: Was it possible for them to meet?
A: No.

Q: Were they of different religions?
A: Yes.

4.21 The Fatal Fare

Q: Did the taxi driver deliberately murder his passenger?
A: Yes.

Q: Was the murdered man a criminal, a spy, or a relative of the driver?
A: No.

Q: Was it a case of mistaken identity?
A: No.

Q: Did either of them have any kind of illness or disability?
A: No.

Q: Was the taxi driver paid for killing the man?
A: No.

Q: Was the time of day important?
A: Yes.

Q: Was the destination important?
A: Yes.

4.22 One Clock

Q: Did he have any kind of radio, television, or other way of knowing the time?
A: No. This was a long time before the invention of any such things.

Q: Did he use the sun or any other external source of information?
A: No.

Q: Did he use his clock at home in the process of determining the correct time?
A: Yes.

Q: Did he set his clock before he left?
A: Yes.

5 Fiendish Puzzlers

5.1 The Man in the Bar I

Q: Was the barman expecting some kind of message or messenger?
A: No.

Q: Was the man expecting the barman to pull a gun?
A: No.

Q: When the man said 'Thank-you,' did he mean that he was grateful?
A: Yes.

Q: Was the barman normal?
A: Yes.

Q: Was the man normal?
A: No. *Clue:* he had an ailment.

5.2 The Man in the Bar II

Q: Did the two men know each other?
A: No, they were complete strangers.

Q: Was the man behind the bar expecting someone?
A: No.

Q: Was there something unusual or threatening about the man who entered the bar?
A: No.

Q: Did the man who entered the bar really want a drink or did he have some other purpose in mind?
A: Yes, he wanted to drink.

Q: Did the man behind the bar mean to kill him?
A: Yes.

Q: Were either of the men criminals?
A: Yes.

Q: Was the man behind the bar the regular barman?
A: No.

5.3 The Man in the Bar III

No clues on this one. You should be an expert on bars by now!

5.4 Another Man in a Bar

Q: Was the brother really guilty of the crimes?
A: Yes.

Q: Were the brothers identical twins?
A: No.

Q: Was it a case of mistaken identity?
A: No.

Q: Was he physically normal?
A: No.

Q: Did the judge choose to not send him to prison because of his brother?
A: Yes.

5.5 The Deadly Block of Wood

Q: Was the man normal?
A: No. *Clue:* If you find his abnormality you are close to solving the problem.

Q: Did his job depend on his abnormality?
A: Yes. *Clue:* he worked in a circus.

Q: Did he use the wood in relation to his work?
A: Yes.

Q: Had the piece of wood been altered?
A: Yes.

Q: Did he commit suicide because he thought his ability to do his job had been affected?
A: Yes.

5.6 The Two Barbers

Q: Was the man making a considered and rational choice in going to the scruffy barber?
A: Yes.

Q: Was his choice governed solely by the desire to get a good haircut?
A: Yes.

Q: Did he make the right decision?
A: Yes.

Q: Had he seen examples of each barber's work?
A: Yes.

5.7 The Mongolian Postal Service

Q: Did he break or bend the flute in any way?
A: No.

Q: Did Boris send it through the Mongolian Postal Service?
A: Yes.

Q: Did he send it in a container that met the rules of not being longer than one metre?
A: Yes.

Q: Do the Mongolian Postal Service officials measure items correctly with a tape measure along each side?
A: Yes.

5.8 Heaven

Q: Was there some physical difference that distinguished them from all others?
A: Yes.

Q: Would it be immediately apparent to any observer?
A: Yes.

Q: Was it related to the fact that they were the first two humans?
A: Yes.

5.9 Fool's Gold

Q: Can the difference between the two cylinders be determined by their physical appearance?
A: No.

Q: Does the solution to this problem involve carrying out some physical test or experiment?
A: Yes.

Q: Is it simple to perform?
A: Yes.

Q: Does it involve weighing the bars or immersing them in liquid?
A: No.

5.10 The Man in the Bar, Again!

Q: Did the barman know or recognize the man?
A: No.

Q: Did the barman think he recognized the man?
A: Yes.

Q: Did the barman deliberately shoot the man?
A: Yes.

Q: Was his motive revenge?
A: Yes.

Q: Was the barman pleased that he had shot the man?
A: At first yes, but later not.

5.11 The Plane Hijacker

Q: Did the man change his mind during the course of the hijack?
A: No.

Q: So he always intended to leap out of the plane on his own?
A: Yes.

Q: Did he carefully choose one parachute in preference to the other?
A: No.

Q: Did he ask for two parachutes in order to deceive the airport authorities?
A: Yes.

Q: Did he do this to protect himself?
A: Yes.

5.12 Wealth Tax

Q: Did the richest man give away all his money?
A: No.

Q: Did he double the wealth of every other citizen?
A: Yes.

Q: Does it matter how many people there are in Lateralia?
A: No.

Q: Did the pattern of distribution of wealth change?
A: No.

Q: Did the ownership of the wealth change?
A: Yes.

Clue: This wealth tax operation could be carried out every year with a new richest citizen giving away his wealth and still it would make no difference to the overall distribution of wealth in Lateralia.

5.13 Death on the Train

Q: Did the man feel suicidal when he boarded the train?
A: No.

Q: Did something happen on the train to cause him to take his life?
A: Yes.

Q: Was anyone else involved?
A: No.

Q: Was the man in good health?
A: No. *Clue:* he had been recently discharged from hospital.

Q: Had he been wearing the large handkerchief?
A: Yes.

Q: Did he commit suicide because he mistakenly thought he had not been cured?
A: Yes.

5.14 The Amorous Commuter

Q: Does he always take the first train to arrive?
A: Yes.

Q: Does he take 11 times as many trains to Slough as he does to Reading?
A: Yes.

Q: In the course of the day, are there the same number of trains from Maidenhead to Reading as from Maidenhead to Slough?
A: Yes.

Q: Does the answer have anything to do with the timing of the trains?
A: Yes.

5.15 Short Roads

It is hard to believe that a solution exists that requires less road than number 3. After all, the diagonals represent the shortest distance between A and C and between B and D. However, the Minister of Finance was correct. There is a solution which links all four towns with less total road. There are no tricks or corny catches involved.

5.16 The Hunter and the Bear

Obviously, if you go one mile south then one east then one north, you finish approximately one mile west of where you started. The reason it is approximately rather than exactly one mile is because you are on a great sphere—the Earth.

If you analyze the problem in terms of the sphere, then it quickly becomes apparent that at the North Pole you can go one mile south, one east, and one north and return to your starting place. Thus, the bear was a polar bear and therefore white. That was the original puzzle. But some bright spark worked out that the North Pole is not the only geographical solution.

Think about the problem again.

5.17 The Arm of the Postal Service.

Q: Did each of the two men have only one arm?
A: Yes.

Q: Did the man who sent the parcel have only one arm?
A: Yes.

Q: Did the sender amputate his own arm before sending it through the post?
A: Yes.

Q: Did he do this willingly?
A: Yes.

Q: Had all three been present when the first two had lost their arms?
A: Yes.

Q: Was it in the form of an accident?
A: No.

5.18 A Weighty Problem I

Believe it or not, it is possible to weigh any amount between 1 and 40 pounds with just four weights. This assumes that you can put the weights on either side of the balance. If you can put the weights in one pan only (because the other is reserved solely for sugar), then you need all of six weights. But with those six, you can weigh any amount of sugar from 1 to 63 pounds. Now you need to apply straightforward mathematical reasoning to identify which weights are needed in each case.

5.19 A Weighty Problem II

This is a very tough problem, but it is solvable with a determined approach. Here are some clues to help you on your way: (1) Every weighing must be designed to yield the maximum amount of information. Therefore, it must be able to offer three possible outcomes—to weigh down to the left or to the right or to balance. (2) If you know that a group of three balls contains the dud ball and you know whether it is heavier or lighter, then you can identify which one it is by weighing any one of the three against any other. (3) Starting with five against five gives you big problems if they do not balance. Similarly, three against three leads to trouble if the first weighing gives a balance. (4) If the scales do not balance, then you know that any balls not on the scales must be true and you can use some or all of those to help in the next weighing.

THE ANSWERS

1 Easy Puzzlers

1.1 The Man in the Elevator

The man is a dwarf. He can reach the button in the elevator for the first floor, but he cannot reach the button for the tenth floor. The seventh floor button is the highest he can reach.

1.2 Bombs Away!

The bomber was flying upside-down!

1.3 The Coal, Carrot, and Scarf

They were used by children who made a snowman. The snow has now melted.

1.4 The Two Americans

They were husband and wife.

1.5 The Man Who Hanged Himself

He climbed on a block of ice, which has since melted.

1.6 The Men in the Hotel

Mr. Jones could not sleep because Mr. Smith was snoring. His phone call awoke Mr. Smith and stopped him snoring long enough for Mr. Jones to get to sleep.

1.7 The Silent Cabbie

He must have heard her initial instructions or he would not have known where to take her.

75

1.8 A Peculiar House

The builder built the house at the North Pole!

1.9 Death in the Phone Booth

He was describing to a friend the size of a fish that got away. In his enthusiasm, he put his hands through the windows, thereby accidentally slitting his wrists.

1.10 The Man in the House

The man was a burglar intent on robbing the house. When he reached the library, he heard a harsh voice say 'Hands up!' When he looked around, he saw a parrot in a cage.

1.11 A Chess Piece

Who said that they were playing each other?

1.12 Happy or Sad

It was the final of the Miss World Beauty Contest. The winner always cries. The disappointed runners-up smile because everyone is watching them and they are expected to look happy and radiant.

1.13 The Unseen Walker

He walked through the sewers.

1.14 The Dream

The sacked employee was the warehouse night watchman. He should have been awake all night on his security duties. Having a dream proved that he was asleep on the job. For this, he was fired.

1.15 In the Pet Shop

There was a price list on the wall. It showed poodle puppies at eight dollars, Labradors at nine dollars, and Alsatians at 10 dollars. The first man put a ten dollar bill on the counter, so he could have wanted any of the three breeds. The second man put down one five dollar bill and five one dollar bills. The assistant correctly deduced that the second man wanted the Alsatian.

1.16 The Coffee Drinker

He had sweetened the original cup of coffee with sugar. He therefore knew when he tasted the coffee that it was the same cup.

1.17 One Step Beyond

He started off outside the window and leapt into the building. Why was he outside? He could either have been on the ledge contemplating suicide or he could have been the window cleaner. Take your pick.

1.18 The Turkish Bath Mystery

John was murdered by Jack, who brought an ice dagger into the Turkish Baths in his thermos flask. The dagger melted away after the murder leaving no clue.

2 Moderate Puzzlers

2.1 Anthony and Cleopatra

Anthony and Cleopatra were goldfish. They died when their bowl was knocked over by a rather clumsy guard dog.

2.2 Five Men

The four men were carrying the fifth man, who was in his coffin.

2.3 Trouble with Sons I

They were two of a set of triplets!

2.4 Trouble with Sons II

The mother was a Russian who was widowed during the war and who had fled to the West, leaving her first son behind with his aunt and uncle. She settled in France, married a Frenchman, and had a second son. When her first son visited her for the first time, there was a tearful reunion around the kitchen table. However, neither half-brother could speak the other's language, so they could converse only through their mother.

2.5 The Two Sisters

When they had finished the cleaning, they had no mirror to look at, so each girl looked at her sister. The girl with the clean face saw that her sister was dirty and assumed that she would be dirty, so she washed. Her sister made the reverse assumption.

2.6 The Miller's Daughter

Her best course of action is to take a stone from the bag and immediately drop it on the path. She can then say, "We can work out the color of the stone I selected by looking at the one that is left. If that is black, I must have selected the white stone."

2.7 Water and Wine

They are both equally contaminated. The water contains exactly as much wine as the wine contains water. The most elegant proof for this celebrated little puzzle is as follows: It does not matter how many transfers are made between the glasses or whether the contents are stirred. Provided that the volumes in the two glasses are equal, then any water not in the water glass must be in the wine, there is nowhere else it can be. The wine that it has replaced must be in the water glass. The water glass therefore contains as much wine as the wine contains water.

2.8 The Man in the Painting

It is the man's son in the painting. 'My father's son' must be the man himself (since he had no brothers or sisters). Therefore, 'this man's father is my father's son' becomes 'this man's father is me'. So, the man in the picture is his son.

2.9 The Single Statement

The explorer made the statement, "I will be eaten by lions." Now, if the chief does feed him to the lions, his statement will have been true, so he should have been thrown off the cliff. But if he is thrown off the cliff, his statement will have been false. The chief had to admit that the only fair course of action was to let the explorer go free.

2.10 Birthday Blues

The statement was made on January the first. Freda's birthday is on December 31st. She was 17 the day before yesterday. She was 18 yesterday. She will be 19 this year and 20 next year.

2.11 The Four Sheep

The sheep are standing on the four corner points of an equal-sided pyramid. Or to put it another way, three are on the points of an equilateral triangle and the other is on a mound of earth in the centre.

2.12 A Geography Question

Remarkable as it may seem, the west end of the Panama Canal is in the Caribbean and the east end in the Pacific. The Isthmus snakes around at that point and the canal runs from north-west (the Caribbean) to south-east (the Pacific). If you still do not believe it, then look it up in a large scale atlas.

2.13 Family Reunion

There was a brother and sister. The brother's son was there and so was the sister's daughter. From this, it follows that the son and daughter were cousins, and all the other relationships are quite straightforward.

2.14 Crossing the Desert

The two trucks were carrying ice. The older truck was less well insulated that the new one. Its ice therefore melted, making the truck lighter. Its tracks therefore faded.

2.15 Old Mrs. Jackson

Old Mrs. Jackson acted as a witness to a document that both the Joneses signed.

2.16 Matrimonial Problems

John and David were both clergymen. David married John to Diana. That is why they share the same anniversary. John married Jane to her husband. On a separate occasion, John married David to his wife.

2.17 The Man with the Wood

The wood was sawdust. He poured it into a square box to make the cube shape, a bucket to make the cylinder, and then into a pyramid-shaped box to make the pyramid.

2.18 Stuck Tight

The little girl suggested that the driver let some air out of the truck's tires. He let out enough to lower the truck by the small amount required to let it pass under the bridge.

2.19 Coming Home

This puzzle depends on the reader making the false assumption that the man was coming home at night. He was returning home in bright sunlight, so anyone could have seen him.

2.20 A Riddle

The answer is a towel.

2.21 Another Riddle

The answer is a coffin.

2.22 The Horse Dyed

Although the dye made the horse harder to see, it also made it much easier to smell. The buffalo caught the scent of the dye from a long distance and made their escape.

2.23 Push That Car

He was playing Monopoly.

2.24 The Unrequested Kiss

She saved the man by giving him the kiss of life, i.e. mouth-to-mouth resuscitation.

2.25 The Two Golfers

They were playing tennis. At 30-all Ben hit a shot out. Archie then served an ace to win the game and match.

3 Historical Puzzlers

3.1 Sew What?

James, Duke of Monmouth, was beheaded on 15 July 1685 after the defeat of his forces at the battle of Sedgemoor, which ended his challenge to the throne of King James II. After his execution, it was belatedly decided that a portrait should be painted. The head was sewn back onto the body, which was dressed so that the artist could begin his work.

3.2 The Grateful Prisoner

Monsieur M. Cyparis was the sole survivor, out of 30,000 people, of the volcanic eruption of Mont Pelee, which destroyed St. Pierre, capital of Martinique in the West Indies on May 8th, 1902. He had been locked in a strong underground jail cell. All the other people in this once-prosperous town were killed by lava, fire, or poisonous gases.

3.3 Ben Jonson

Ben Jonson, being second only to Shakespeare in his eminence as a poet at that time, was buried in the Poets' Corner in Westminster Abbey. The plot that was allocated to him was so small that he had to be buried in a sitting position in order to fit in it.

3.4 Lord Strathallen

Lord Strathallen was mortally wounded during the battle of Culloden Moor on April 16th, 1746, when the Scots under Bonnie Prince Charlie were defeated by the Duke of Cumberland to end the "Forty-five" rebellion. Lord Strathallen was a Catholic and asked for the Holy Eucharist before he died. The priest could find no bread and wine, so he consecrated oatcake and whiskey instead.

3.5 A Remarkable Journey

They hold the world record for the longest journey driven in reverse. Charles Creighton and James Hargis drove their Ford Model A in reverse all the way from New York to Los Angeles between 26 July and 13 August, 1930. They then drove back to New York again in reverse!

3.6 The Two Writers

The woman was George Eliot, the authoress who was born Mary Ann Evans in 1819 and who took her pen name in order to promote her literary career. She died in 1880, the same year that she married John Cross.

Evelyn Waugh was born in 1903 and he died in 1966.

3.7 World War I

The number of recorded head injuries increased, but the number of deaths decreased. Previously, if a soldier had been hit on the head by a piece of shrapnel, it would have pierced his cap and probably killed him. This would have been recorded as a death, not a head injury. After helmets were issued it was more likely that a fragment of shrapnel would cause an injury rather than death. Thus, the incidence of head injuries increased, while the incidence of deaths decreased.

3.8 King George IV

He had a right boot and a left boot! Until that time, all shoes or boots were made to be worn on either foot.

3.9 Walk This Way

He walked all the way on his hands, and thereby set the world duration record for walking on hands.

4 Difficult Puzzlers

4.1 Death in a Field

The man had jumped from a plane, but his parachute had failed to open. It was the unopened package by his side.

4.2 Death in Rome

Mr. Jones was a travel agent. He had recently supplied by post two plane tickets for a Mr. Rigby-Brown. The two tickets were for Rome, but the one for Mr. Rigby-Brown had been ordered as a return ticket. Mrs. Rigby-Brown's ticket had been one way only.

4.3 Woman on the Bridge I

The woman waited until the sentry went into his hut. She then sneaked onto the bridge and walked towards the Swiss border. She walked for nearly three minutes, then she turned around and started to walk back towards Germany. The guard came out and saw her. When she reached him he saw that she had no authority to enter Germany, and he therefore ordered her to go back—to Switzerland!

4.4 Woman on the Bridge II

She juggled the balls as she went over the bridge.

4.5 Trouble with Sons, Again!

For two children, there are only four possible combinations:

	Older	Younger
A	Boy	Boy
B	Boy	Girl
C	Girl	Boy
D	Girl	Girl

Each of these combinations is equally likely (i.e. there is a one in four chance that any two-child family will have one of the above combinations).

For Mrs. Jones, the possibilities are narrowed down to A B or C and of these, only A means that both are boys. Therefore, the chance that both her children are boys is one in three.

For Mrs. Brown, A and C are the only possibilities. There is thus a one in two chance that both her children are boys.

4.6 Silence on the Train

The man was a moderately well-known author. He sat in the carriage and started to chew gum. The woman was deaf and mute and thought he might be speaking to her. She gave him pen and paper on which to write his message. He, being rather vain, thought she had recognized him as a celebrity and wanted his autograph. He signed the paper. His signature meant nothing to her, so she threw the piece of paper away as soon as she left the train.

4.7 The Lonely Man

He was a lighthouse keeper, and the house in which he lived was a lighthouse on a remote outcrop of rock. When he left the place and turned the lights off, the warning to shipping was removed. A shipwreck occurred resulting in the deaths of 90 people.

4.8 The Distant Image

What he could see 40 feet away was the reflection of his hand. There were mirrors on opposite sides of the room. The man held his hand up and slightly to the side of him. He could see its image reflected many times in the mirror in front of him. The first reflection is 20 feet away, the second is 40 feet away, an so on.

4.9 Coins of the Realm

Why are 20 pennies worth more than 15 pennies? Because there are five more of them! The same is true for 1988 pennies and 1983 pennies. The trouble is caused because the brain automatically sees these numbers as dates.

4.10 Baby Has Lots

A baby is born with some 350 separate bones. As the baby grows, some of these bones join together so that in maturity the same person has only some 206 bones.

4.11 The Hotel Detective

The lawyer and the accountant were women. The postman was therefore the only person who could have been called John.

4.12 Faster Than the Speed of Sound

The first man-made object to travel faster than the speed of sound was the tip of a whip. The characteristic noise of the crack of a whip is the result of the tip breaking the sound barrier.

4.13 Concorde

He lived in New York. His wife saw him off from New York in the morning and greeted him on his return in the evening.

4.14 Asphyxiation

The woman lit the oven and then fell asleep on the bed. Her husband simply turned off the main gas supply into the house and then turned it on again a few moments later. This caused the fire to go out. The gas then filled the room and asphyxiated the unfortunate woman.

4.15 The Slow Mover

The answer is Niagara Falls. It is estimated that the Falls started about seven miles further downstream and have cut their way through the rock. They have therefore moved upstream at a rate of several feet a year ever since.

4.16 Dinner for Three

The shepherd who had three loaves should get one coin and the shepherd who had five loaves should get seven coins.

If there were eight loaves and three men, each man ate two and two-thirds loaves. So the first shepherd gave the hunter one-third of a loaf and the second shepherd gave the hunter two and one-third loaves. The shepherd who gave one-third of a loaf should get one coin and the one who gave seven-thirds of a loaf should get seven coins.

4.17 A Theological Puzzle

The answer was 'an equal.' Other possible answers include a parent or a superior being. However, an equal is the most elegant response.

4.18 It's a Knock-out!

He had been trying to break the shop window in order to rob the shop. He threw a brick at the window but, unfortunately for him, the window was made of reinforced glass. The brick rebounded and knocked him out!

4.19 The Frustrated Policemen

His house is built on the border between Venezuela and Colombia. Although his front door and kitchen are in Venezuela, his bedroom lies in Colombian territory. The Venezuelan police have no jurisdiction in Colombia, so they cannot arrest him as long as he stays in his bedroom.

4.20 Neighbors

Ali was a Muslim, Ben a Jew, and Cyril was Christian. Ali was born in 1309 of the Muslim calendar. The starting point for the Muslim calendar is the emigration of Muhammad from Mecca to Medina in AD 622. Consequently, the Muslim year 1309 equates to 1930 A.D. Similarly, Ben's birthdate falls under the Jewish calendar, which started in 3761 B.C. So Ben was born over 3,000 years before Cyril, who in turn was born 619 years before Ali.

4.21 The Fatal Fare

The customer gave as his destination the taxi driver's home address. The driver had known for some time that his wife had a lover who visited her in the afternoons. He deduced that this was his wife's lover, and therefore murdered him.

4.22 One Clock

He wound his clock and set it at some particular time before he left. He noted the exact time of his arrival at and departure from his friend's house. He noted the time showing on his clock when he returned. He walked at the same pace on the two journeys. The elapsed time on his clock is the duration of the two journeys plus the length of his visit to his friend. Knowing the time he spent with his friend, he subtracts this from the elapsed time on his clock and divides the result by two in order to calculate the duration of the journey. He adds this to the exact time he left his friend's house in order to set his clock at the correct time. For example, assume he set his clock at 12, arrived at his friend's at 6:30, and left at 7:30. When he returned, his clock showed 4:00. Then his journey took one and one-half hours and the correct time is 9:00.

5 Fiendish Puzzlers

5.1 The Man in the Bar I

The man had hiccups. The barman recognized this from his speech and drew the gun to give the man a shock. It worked and cured the hiccups, so the man was grateful (and no longer needed the water).

5.2 The Man in the Bar II

The man behind the bar was in the process of robbing the place. He had already shot the barman and he shot the man entering the bar to escape and to avoid recognition.

88

5.3 The Man in the Bar III

It was an iron bar! (*Ouch!*)

5.4 Another Man in a Bar

The guilty man was a Siamese twin, joined at the waist to his brother. The judge could not send the guilty twin to prison without unfairly sentencing the innocent brother.

5.5 The Deadly Block of Wood

The man was a midget who worked in a circus as a star attraction because of his billing as the world's smallest dwarf. Each day, he measured himself with a piece of wood that was exactly his height. One day, a rival dwarf mischievously sawed two inches from the piece of wood. The man mistakenly thought he had grown and would therefore lose his fame and status as the world's smallest dwarf, so he committed suicide.

5.6 The Two Barbers

The traveller deduced, correctly, that since there were only two barbers in the town, each must cut the other's hair. Therefore, the smart barber cut the scruffy barber's hair untidily. The scruffy barber gave the smart barber his tidy haircut. The traveller therefore chose the scruffy barber as the one who would give the best haircut.

5.7 The Mongolian Postal Service

Boris placed the flute diagonally in a suitcase that measured 1 metre by 1 metre. This suitcase was quite acceptable to the postal officials because its sides measured 1 metre. From corner to corner, it measures 1.414 metres—the square root of two.

Incidentally, if his flute had measured 1.7 metres, he could have fitted it across the diagonal of a box whose sides were 1 metre long. The diagonal of a cube is the square root of three times its side—1.73 metres.

From a theoretical mathematical viewpoint, there is no reason why this process cannot be extended indefinitely. If Boris could construct a four dimensional box with 1 metre sides, then he could get a 2 metre flute in it (square root of 4) and a 25 dimensional construction could contain a 5 metre flute while still meeting the rules of having no side longer than 1 metre!

5.8 Heaven

Adam and Eve were the only people there without navels. Because they were not born, they had never had umbilical cords and, therefore, did not have 'belly buttons.'

5.9 Fool's Gold

The easiest solution is to roll both cylinders across the floor. The hollow cylinder will roll farther than the solid one. Its mass is distributed away from its middle, giving it, in terms of physics, a higher moment of inertia than the solid cylinder. Many experiments involving rotating the cylinders would reveal the hollow cylinder, but rolling them is the simplest approach.

5.10 Man in Bar, Again!

The barman's daughter had been murdered by the identical twin of the man who entered the bar. The murderer had been acquitted because of a technicality. (e.g. an illegal search by the police). So the barman longed for revenge. He had seen the murderer in court. He did not know that the murderer had a twin, and, consequently, he shot an innocent man who had entered his bar by chance.

5.11 The Plane Hijacker

The hijacker asked for two parachutes (it is believed) in order to deceive the authorities into thinking that he intended to take a hostage. They therefore gave him two good parachutes. Had he asked for one only, they would have known it was for him and could have given him a dud parachute with a hole in it. By asking for two, he eliminated that risk. Once he knew he had two good parachutes, either would do for his escape.

5.12 Wealth Tax

If there were n inhabitants, and the poorest man owned wealth to the value of $x, then the riches of the citizens in ascending sequence were: $x, 2x, 4x, 8x, 16x, 32x, \ldots 2^{n-1}x$.

Thus, when the richest man has given away the sum of all preceding amounts in the sequence, he is left with just $x. He therefore becomes the poorest man and everyone else, having doubled their fortune, moves one place up the ladder. However, the overall distribution of wealth in the country has not changed, only the owners have.

If you want to test this, then try the model with just five citizens owning $1, $2, $4, $8, $16.

5.13 Death on the Train

The man had just completed a course of treatment intended to cure him of blindness. He had high hopes of success. He travelled home on the train with the handkerchief as a blindfold to protect his eyes from the light.

He could not wait and decided to remove the blindfold to test his eyesight. When he removed the blindfold, he could see nothing and assumed that the treatment had failed. He could not face the future as a blind man and, therefore, he stepped out of the speeding train to his death.

The treatment had, in fact, been successful, but he had unfortunately removed the blindfold while the train was in a long tunnel. The carriage was in complete darkness.

5.14 The Amorous Commuter

The Slough trains depart from Maidenhead at five past every hour. The Reading Trains depart at ten past the hour.

If John arrives at any time between ten past the hour and five past the next hour, then the first train to arrive will be bound for Slough. He will catch the Reading train only if he happens to arrive between five past and ten past the hour. It is therefore 11 times more likely that he will catch the Slough train than the Reading train.

5.15 Short Roads

The shortest solution is shown. It represents some 27.3 miles of road in total and therefore saves a precious mile in road-building expense compared to the two diagonals. Someone starting from A would have a shorter journey to D but a longer one to B or C.

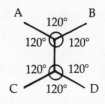

5.16 The Hunter and the Bear

Plainly, the North Pole is one answer to this question. However, it is not the only answer. The other points all lie close to the South Pole.

Any point one mile due north of a circle around the earth with a circumference of exactly one mile will meet the conditions. This circle lies approximately 0.16 miles north of the South Pole.

Starting one mile north of this circle, you could walk one mile south, one mile east (or west), which would take you exactly round the earth to the same point, and then one mile north, which would bring you back to your original starting point.

Similarly, any point one mile due north of a circle of circumference 0.5 miles or 0.25 miles or 0.125 miles etc. would work equally. There are indeed an infinite number of points all less than 1.2 miles from the South Pole that would satisfy the requirements of the problem.

In any event, the bear would still be white, because only polar bears could survive such cold. There are supposed to be no polar bears at the South Pole, but that may be a false assumption!

5.17 The Arm of the Postal Service

The three men had been together on a flying mission in the Pacific. Their plane had come down and they were adrift for many days in a dinghy. They had had some water but no food and were gradually starving to death. Eventually, out of desperation, they agreed to amputate their left arms in order to eat them. They swore a solemn oath that each would have his left arm cut off. One of the three was a doctor and he amputated the arms of one and then later of the other of his colleagues. Just before his turn came, they were rescued. However, his oath was still binding and he later had to have his arm amputated and sent to his colleagues for them to see that the oath had been kept.

5.18 A Weighty Problem I

If the weights can be placed in either of the scale pans, then you can solve the problem with weights of 1, 3, 9, and 27 pounds only. With that combination, any weight from 1 to 40 pounds can be measured.

If the weights can be placed in one scale pan only, then you need the weights 1, 2, 4, 8, 16, and 32 pounds, which enables you to measure any weight up to 63 pounds. This latter solution is really an example of counting with a binary number system where any number can be expressed as the sum of 2 raised to various powers. For example, 63 expressed in binary form is 111111.

5.19 A Weighty Problem II

Let us call the balls A, B, C, D......L. Start by weighing four against four. If they balance, then weigh any of the remaining three against any three of the good balls. If they balance then we know the odd one is the remaining ball and we can identify whether it is heavier or lighter in the final weighing. If the three against three do not balance than we take the three containing the odd ball and weigh any one against another.

If the first weighing of four against four does not produce a balance, then the second weighing involves three against three with balls switched between the two pans and a good ball introduced So:

If $\quad$ $A + B + C + D > E + F + G + H$

We try $\quad$ $A + B + E$ against $C + F + J$

If $\quad$ $A + B + E = C + F + J$ then we know that either D is heavier or G or H is lighter, so we weigh G against H.

If $\quad$ $A + B + E > C + F + J$ then we know that either F is lighter or A or B is heavier, so we weigh A against B.

If $\quad$ $A + B + E < C + F + J$ then we know that either E is lighter or C is heavier, so we weigh either against a good ball: e.g., K against E.

An alternative second weighing is $A + B + E$ against $C + D + F$, which follows similar lines to the above.

ABOUT THE AUTHOR

Paul Sloane was born in Scotland in 1950. He was brought up in the north of England and went to Trinity Hall, Cambridge University, where he took a first-class honors degree in Engineering. While at Cambridge, he met his wife, who is a teacher. They live in Farnborough, England, with their three daughters.

Paul Sloane's career has been mainly in computer sales and marketing. He is now the Managing Director of a personal computer software company. His job involves considerable travel within Europe and the USA. His hobbies include reading, golf, music, and chess. He has always had a keen interest in puzzles and he tries out new problems mercilessly on his daughters. Amazingly, they seem to thrive on it!

INDEX

CHALLENGING

LATERAL THINKING PUZZLES

by Paul Sloane and Des MacHale

*With acknowledgments to Ajaz Ahmed for "Deduction,"
Andy Balchin for "How to Hug," and Erwin Brecher for
"The Stranger in the Car."*

Edited by Claire Bazinet

*This book is dedicated
to our long-suffering wives,
Ann Sloane and Anne MacHale,
in appreciation
of their patience and support.*

CONTENTS

INTRODUCTION

It is said that when the North American Indians first saw a man riding a horse they assumed that it was some new creature with four legs and two arms. Very often when we face a new situation or problem we fall back on prior experiences and form quick but incorrect judgments. We assume too much, ask too few questions, and jump to the wrong conclusions.

This book should provide an amusing antidote to any bad habits of lazy or inflexible thinking. The puzzles will probably provide the most entertainment and brain-flexing value if attempted in a small group. One person knows the solution and the others, whether family, friends, or colleagues, ask questions in order to determine the answer. In the strictest form of this game the "Chairperson" can give one of three answers, only, to any question: yes, no, or irrelevant. The most successful questioners are those who are imaginative and logical, who test all assumptions and then try to narrow down the area of search with broad questions before homing in on specific details. In the right company, the game can be frustrating, stimulating, hilarious, and rewarding.

The puzzles generally do not have obscure solutions or need specialist knowledge. They are not designed to deliberately mislead the reader. The exceptions are the "WALLY Tests," which consist of special questions employing every low trick to catch you out.

These puzzles are meant to test your powers of questioning, deduction, and persistence. If at first the direct approach leads nowhere, try coming at the problem from the side; in other words, lateral thinking. Be flexible. Don't look straight at the answers or you will miss most of the fun. When you do get frustrated try the clues section for some help. Remember that in real life there are no answers at the back of the book. Enjoy the puzzles!

THE PUZZLES

1   Easy Puzzles

1.1   The Apple Problem

There were six apples in a basket and six girls in the room. Each girl took one apple, yet one apple remained in the basket. How come?

1.2 The Two Presidents

The 22nd and 24th presidents of the United States had the same mother and the same father, but were not brothers. How could this be so?

1.3 Game, Set, and Match

Two men were playing tennis. They played five sets and each man won three sets. How did they do this?

1.4 Wondrous Walk

A man walked all the way from Dublin to Cork along main roads without passing a single pub. How did he manage that? (Pubs or "public houses," that is, bars, are very common in Ireland.)

1.5 Father and Son

William's father was older than his grandfather. How did that happen?

1.6 The Amazing Fall

A man who was not wearing a parachute jumped out of a plane. He landed on hard ground yet he was unhurt. Why?

1.7 Shopping Is Good for You

A man got up at 9 a.m. He became so engrossed in his newspaper he did not have time to go out and shop as he had planned. At 11 a.m. he went for a flying lesson. He carefully followed all the instructions given to him by his instructor until he came in to land. He then ignored his instructor and crashed the plane killing them both. The accident would not have happened if he had gone shopping, which just goes to show how important shopping can be. Why should this be so?

8

1.8 Your Turn to Drive

Two brothers were talking. One said, "I am fed up with living in Birmingham because I have to drive all the time. Why don't we move to London?" His brother replied, "But that would mean that I would have to drive all the time." Why was this true?

1.9 See Saw

A deaf man needed to buy a saw to cut some wood. He went into a hardware store. How did he indicate to the storekeeper that he wanted to buy a saw?

1.10 The Two Lookouts

Two sentries were on duty outside a barracks. One faced up the road to watch for anyone approaching from the north. The other looked down the road to see if anyone approached from the south. Suddenly one of them said to the other, "Why are you smiling?" How did he know that his companion was smiling?

1.11 The Deadly Drive

A man drove to and from work every day along a dangerous and twisty mountain road. However, he knew the road very well so could drive quickly yet safely. One day, while he was at work, his car was broken into and several items were stolen. As the car was not damaged the man got in and started driving. He never reached home. His car swerved off the road and he was killed. Why?

1.12 Another Man in an Elevator

Bill was on holiday. He stayed on the fifth floor of a hotel. Every morning at 8 a.m. he took the elevator down to the lobby on the first floor, had breakfast, and then took the elevator back up to the fifth floor. Every evening at 8 p.m. he took the elevator down to the lobby and then he walked up the five flights of stairs and went back to his room. He did not like walking up all those stairs, so why did he do it?

1.13 Growing Younger

Ben was 20 years old in 1980 but only 15 years old in 1985. How come?

1.14 The Habitual Walker

A deaf man was very regular in his habits. He arose every morning at 7:35 a.m. and set off for his half-hour morning walk at 7:45. In the course of this walk he went over a level

10

railroad crossing but he knew that he was quite safe because the first train did not come by until 9 a.m. One morning, although he followed his routine exactly, he was run over by a train at the crossing. What went wrong?

1.15 Greenland

Greenland is a huge country covered with snow and ice. Why did the man who discovered it call it Greenland?

1.16 Radio On

A young girl was listening to the radio. Suddenly it went off for a minute and then came back on again. There was nothing wrong with the radio or with the program transmission from the radio station. She did not touch the radio controls. Why did it go off and on?

1.17   The Boxing Match

At the end of a long hard boxing match one boxer was knocked out by the other. The judges agreed it was a completely proper victory. Yet during the course of the match no man threw a punch. What happened?

1.18   The Nephew

A man and his sister were out shopping one day when the man said, "That boy over there is my nephew." "That is right," replied his sister, "but he is not my nephew." How come?

1.19   Barrel Trouble

A man filled an empty barrel. It was then lighter than when he started. What did he fill it with?

1.20   Rival Fans

One day, in a crowded room, a supporter of the Brazilian soccer team saw a supporter of his team's great rivals, Argentina. The Brazilian fan walked over to the Argentinian fan and struck him a fierce blow. The Argentinian fan who had been knocked flat got up from the floor, turned around, and then thanked the man who had hit him. Why?

1.21   Coming Up for Air

As part of a school experiment a girl was sent to the middle of a nearby city with instructions to collect a sample so that pollution levels could be measured. She was given a glass container with a removable but tight-fitting lid. Of course she noticed that the jar contained comparatively clean air from the school environment. How did she ensure that she excluded this air and retrieved an absolutely accurate sample of the city air?

1.22 Nuts Away!

A man was changing a wheel on his car when the four nuts used to hold the wheel in place fell into a sewer drain and were lost. He was afraid he was stuck there, but a passing boy made a very useful suggestion which enabled the man to drive off. What was the boy's idea?

1.23 The Golf Pro

Although there are very few golf tour professionals who are left-handed, most clubs prefer to have left-handed golf pros as instructors. Why?

1.24   Deduction

A man suspected his wife of having an affair. One day he told her that he had been suddenly called away on business and would be out of town for a few days. He then left the house but returned an hour later. His wife was not there but he quickly discovered the name and address of her lover. How?

The WALLY Test

Now that you have warmed up with the Easy Puzzles you are ready to try your wits on the first official World Association for Laughter, Learning, and Youth (WALLY) Test. Get a pencil and paper. You must answer each question immediately after reading it. You have 4 minutes to complete the test and you are not allowed to change any answer once it is written. Do not look at the solutions until you have answered all the questions.

(a) Write your name in the square provided.

(b) Take two apples from five apples. How many do you have?

(c) Do they have Fourth of July in England?

(d) If you had only one match and entered a dark room containing an oil lamp, a newspaper, and some kindling wood, what would you light first?

(e) A farmer had 17 sheep. All but 9 died. How many did he have left?

(f) How many animals of each species did Moses take into the Ark?

(g) A plane full of English tourists flies from Holland to Spain. It crashes in France. Where should the survivors be buried?

(h) If a redhouse is made of red wood and a whitehouse is made of white wood, what is a greenhouse made of?

(i) If Mr. Jones' peacock laid an egg in Mr. Brown's garden, who is the rightful owner of the egg?

(j) Mrs. Taylor's bungalow is decorated entirely in pink. Her lamps, walls, carpets, and ceilings are all pink. What color are her stairs?

(k) If you drive a bus with 42 people on board from Boston to Washington, D.C., and drop off 3 people at each of six stops and pick up 4 people at half the stops, when you arrive at Washington 10 hours later what is the driver's name?

(l) Write this down as one number: 15 thousand, 15 hundred, and 15.

(m) What do Kermit the Frog and Attila the Hun have in common?

(n) What do you sit on, sleep on, and brush your teeth with?

(o) How many times can you take 3 from 25?

See WALLY Test solution on page 18.

2 Moderate Puzzles

2.1 The Penny Black

The famous Penny Black, the world's first postage stamp, was introduced in England in 1840. The idea of postage stamps was a great success and was taken up worldwide. Yet the Penny Black was in use for only one year before it was replaced by the Penny Red. Why?

2.2 Flat Tire I

A man woke up one morning to find that one of the wheels of his car had a completely flat tire. Despite this he set off in his car and drove 100 miles to visit a customer. He then drove 100 miles home. He did not repair or inflate the flat tire. How did he manage to make the journey?

2.3 Flat Tire II

Four college students arrived late for a lecture, explaining to their instructor that their car had suffered a flat tire on the way there. How did the clever lecturer immediately show those assembled that the late arrivals were not telling the truth?

2.4 Bottled Fruit

We all know that there's a way to get a ship into a bottle. How would you get a full-sized pear into a bottle without damaging the pear or breaking or cutting the bottle?

2.5 The Cowboy's Fate

Cowboys who lived in the Wild West led a dangerous existence. They were at risk from cattle stampedes, Indian attacks, rattlesnakes, disease, and gunfights. However, none of these was the usual cause of death, which was something routine but deadly. What was the most common cause of death among cowboys?

2.6 The Village Idiot

Visitors to a scenic mountain village were often amused by the village idiot. When offered a choice between a shiny 50-cent piece and a crumpled $5 bill, he would always happily choose the half-dollar. The bill was worth ten times as much, so why did he never choose it?

2.7 The Island Fire

A man is on an island which is one mile long and about 100 yards wide. The grass and shrubs are very dry from a long drought. Suddenly, a fire starts at one end of the island. It is racing towards him along the width of the island fanned by a strong wind blowing in his direction. He cannot take refuge in the sea because it is infested with sharks. There is no beach, just sheer cliffs. What can he do to avoid being consumed in the flames?

2.8 The Sleepy Kings

On one occasion King George II of England went to sleep on the night of September 2 and did not wake up until the morning of September 14. His doctors and advisors were not particularly worried by this. Maybe this was because they knew that a similar sort of thing had once happened to King Henry III of France. He had fallen asleep on December 9 and not woken until December 20. We know that monarchs in those days had a pretty easy life, but what was going on here?

2.9 The Portrait

A man stands looking at a portrait and says, "Sons and brothers have I none, but this person's father is my father's son." Who is in the portrait?

The WALLY Test Answers

Total up your number of correct answers. Then see where you fit on this table:

Score	Official Rating
10–15	Smart Alec
5–9	Wally
0–4	Mega Wally

(a) What square?
(b) Two apples.
(c) Yes.
(d) The match.
(e) Nine.
(f) None (it was Noah's Ark).
(g) Survivors are not buried.
(h) Glass.
(i) Peacocks do not lay eggs.
(j) There are no stairs in a bungalow.
(k) Your name.
(l) 16,515.
(m) The same middle name—"the."
(n) A chair, a bed, and a toothbrush.
(o) Once.

18

2.10 Winning Isn't Everything

Three friends, Alf, Bert, and Chris, played golf every Saturday for a year. The games were friendly but competitive. They all had the same handicap so whoever took the least strokes won the game and whoever took the most strokes came last. At the end of the year they compared scores to see who was the best and a furious row broke out. Alf pointed out that he had finished ahead of Bert more often than he had finished behind him. Bert countered that he had finished ahead of Chris more often than he had finished behind him and that Chris had finished ahead of Alf more often than he had finished behind him. How could this be so?

19

2.11 The Reluctant Diner

A businessman came home as usual at 5 P.M. He normally ate dinner as soon as he arrived home. This evening he was very hungry as he had had no lunch. However, despite the fact that all his favorite foods were available and ready to be eaten, he waited until exactly 8 P.M. before dining alone. Why did he wait?

2.12 Death in a Car

A man went out for a drive. A day later he was found dead in the car. The car had not crashed. How had he died?

2.13 Last Cord

A man lies dead in a field. Next to him is a long piece of cord. How did he die?

2.14 Saturday Flights

A man flew into Los Angeles on Saturday. He stayed for three nights at the Beverly Hills Hotel, then spent one night in the Santa Monica Hilton. He then flew out again on Saturday. Between the two flights he never left the Los Angeles area and he did not stay anywhere except those two hotels. How could he arrive and leave on Saturday, yet stay only four nights?

2.15 The Trains That Did Not Crash

A single train track runs through a tunnel which goes from east to west. One afternoon two trains run along the track at the same speed and enter the tunnel, one going east and the other going west. Neither stops or changes speed, yet they do not crash. Why not?

2.16 Copyright

How do the publishers of dictionaries or atlases protect themselves from pirates who would copy their work?

2.17   The Ransom

A rich man's son was kidnapped. The ransom note told
him to bring a valuable diamond to a phone booth in the
middle of a public park. Plainclothes police officers sur-
rounded the park, intending to follow the criminal or his
messenger. The rich man arrived at the phone booth and
followed instructions but the police were powerless to prevent the diamond from leaving the park and reaching the
crafty villain. What did he do?

2.18   Moving Parts

Two common objects carry out the same function. One of
the objects has many thousands of moving parts while the
other object has no moving parts. What are the objects?

2.19   An Early Burial

John Brown died on Thursday, December 6, and was buried the same week—on Wednesday, December 5, to be precise. How did that happen?

2.20   Trouble and Strife

Mrs. White was happily knitting while her husband watched television. Suddenly the phone rang. Mr. White answered it. He was angry because it was a wrong number, but she was even more angry. Why?

2.21   Bath Water

Some time ago, before central heating and water boilers, people would heat water on stoves. At that time a scullery maid was heating a large pan of water in order to add it to a bathtub which contained some water at room temperature. When the butler saw it he told her off. "Don't you realize," he said, "that the longer you heat that water on the stove the colder the bath will be when you pour the hot water in?" He was right. Why?

2.22   The Hold-Up

A man parked his car outside a bank and rushed in. He held up twenty-five people and ran out with $200. A policeman who saw the whole incident stopped the man. He told him off and then let him go. Why?

2.23   The Worst Sailor

Jim was one of the worst sailors on board ship. He was surly, lazy, untrustworthy, uncooperative, and always causing trouble. Yet the ship's captain often said of him, "I wish we had ten men like Jim." Why?

2.24 The Valuable Book

A man had a book which was worth $40,000. Why did he deliberately destroy it?

3 Difficult Puzzles

3.1 Cuddly Bears

At a children's hospital the patients loved to play with the cuddly teddy bears they had there. Unfortunately, the children liked them so much that the bears were disappearing at an alarming rate as the young patients took them home. How did the hospital solve this problem?

3.2   The High-Society Dinner

At a fancy, upper-class dinner party a precious gold coin was being passed around the table for inspection when suddenly the lights went out. When the lights came on again the coin was missing. A search of each guest was ordered. One man refused to be searched. The police were called but before they arrived the missing coin was found under a saucer. Why did the guest refuse to be searched?

3.3   Eight Years Old

A girl was eight years old on her first birthday. How could that be?

3.4   Cover That Hole

A manhole is a hole which allows someone to gain access to the sewers or other pipes which are below ground. Our local town council recently decided that all the town's manhole covers should be changed from square to round ones. We are used to the town council making silly decisions, but this time they were absolutely right. Why?

3.5   The Protagoras Paradox

Protagoras was a lawyer in ancient Greece. As an act of kindness he took on a poor but promising young man as a pupil. He agreed to teach him law but make no charge until the student had won his first case, when the student would repay his tuition fees. The young man gladly agreed to this plan. The student completed his training, then decided that he did not wish to practise law. Instead, he retired to the countryside to keep goats. Protagoras was disgusted at this waste of talent and training and dismayed that he would not be reimbursed for the tuition. He decided to sue his pupil in order to recover his fees. If the two men met in court to argue the case, who do you think would have won?

3.6 Hand in Glove

A French glove manufacturer received an order for 5,000 pairs of expensive sealskin gloves from a New York department store. He then learned that there was a very expensive tax on the import of sealskin gloves into the United States. How did he (legitimately) get the gloves into the country without paying the import tax?

3.7 The School Superintendent

A visiting school superintendent noticed that whenever he asked one class a question all the children would put up their hands. Moreover, although the teacher always chose a different child to answer, the answer was always correct. Why?

3.8 No Trumps

Can you resolve this argument which arose at a recent bridge match? Spades were trumps. Which is more likely: that a pair of players will have no spades dealt to them or all the spades dealt to them?

3.9 How to Beat Nick Faldo

A man challenged the Masters Golf champion to a round of golf on the condition that he be allowed to chose the time and place of their contest. The champion accepted the challenge but was easily defeated by the challenger. Why?

3.10 How to Beat Carl Lewis

A man challenged the Olympic 100-metres sprint champion to a race over a short distance on the condition that he be allowed to choose the course. How does the man manage to beat the champion? (N.B.: The solution to the preceding problem won't help you here.)

3.11 The Missing Furniture

A man was doing his job but was killed because he lacked a certain piece of furniture. Why?

3.12 The Dead Man

A man lies dead in a room, with a cord tied tightly around his neck. The door has been locked from the inside. Outside of the body, there is nothing else in the room. Remembering that one cannot choke oneself (one would pass out before dying), how did he die?

3.13 The Busy Hospital

St. James Hospital handled all the accident cases for the

city. They were kept especially busy by the large number of drivers and passengers injured on the city's roads. To improve road safety, a law was passed making the wearing of seat belts mandatory. Drivers and passengers now started to wear seat belts in their cars. The frequency of road accidents remained exactly the same. However, the hospital was now even busier handling road-accident victims than before. Why?

3.14 The Fallen Sign

A man was walking in country unfamiliar to him. He came to a crossroads where he found that the signpost showing the directions of the roads had fallen over. How did he find out which way to go?

3.15   False Fingerprints

A man stabbed his wife to death. He was alone with his victim before and after the crime. To throw the police off the scent he suddenly decided to leave false fingerprints on the murder weapon. How did he do it?

3.16   Found, Lost, Found

A man threw something away. He then paid someone else twenty dollars to try to find it but the search was unsuccessful. Later the man found it easily himself. How?

3.17   The Crippled Child

A child was born with its legs so wasted that it would never be able to walk. When they learned this, the child's parents were especially happy that the child was crippled rather than normal and healthy. Why?

3.18   Insurance

A man's lifelong ambition was to achieve a certain goal, yet he insured himself against achieving it. What was the goal?

3.19   Eggs

Ornithologists now agree that there is a very good reason why birds' eggs are generally narrower at one end than the other. What is the reason?

3.20   The Guard Dog

A landowner boasted that nobody could enter his orchard because of the fierce dog he had guarding it. How did a crafty boy safely gain entrance without damaging the dog in any way?

3.21 The Last Message

A man was found shot dead in his study. He was slumped over his desk and a gun was in his hand. There was a cassette recorder on his desk. When the police entered the room and pressed the play button on the tape recorder they heard, "I can't go on. I have nothing to live for." Then there was the sound of a gunshot. How did the detective immediately know that the man had been murdered?

3.22 The Japanese Speaker

A Los Angeles businessman took great pains to learn Japanese from a native speaker of the language. He became fluent; his vocabulary and grammar were excellent and his accent was good. When he later went to Japan and started speaking Japanese with a group of businessmen there, they could hardly contain their surprise and amusement at the way he spoke. Why?

The Advanced WALLY Test

Before you tackle the next section, Fiendish Puzzles, let's see what you have learned. Get a pencil and paper. You have 4 minutes to complete this advanced WALLY test and you are not allowed to change any answer once it is written. Do not look at the solutions until you have answered all the questions.

(a) John is a popular boys' name in the United States, and many Spanish boys are called José. What is a boy commonly called in France?

(b) To enter the water, why do scuba divers sit on the edge of the boat and fall out backwards?

(c) Is it legal to marry your widow's sister?

(d) If you started in Houston, Texas, to dig a hole through the center of the earth where would you come out?

(e) If folk is spelled F O L K and joke is spelled J O K E, how do you spell the word for the white of an egg?

(f) You have two notes in your wallet for a total of $101. One of them is not a $1 bill. What are they?

(g) What could you be sure to find right in the middle of Toronto?

(h) A daddy bull drinks 10 gallons of water per hour and a baby bull drinks 4 gallons. How much would a mommy bull drink?

(i) Who was the last man to box Joe Louis?

(j) Is it likely or unlikely that the next U.S. men's tennis champion will have more than the average number of arms?

(k) A man was walking across a bridge in Paris when he saw his wife on the other side of the bridge with her lover. The man drew a gun and shot his wife. The recoil from the gun caused him to fall off the bridge and drown. He was tried for murder. What was the jury's verdict?

(l) How many grooves are there on the average long-playing record?

(m) Some months have 30 days and some have 31 days. How many have 28 days?

(n) Farmer Giles has three black pigs, two brown pigs, and one pink pig. How many of Farmer Giles' pigs could say that they are the same color as another of Farmer Giles' pigs?

(o) A rope ladder over the side of a ship has rungs which are 1 foot (.3 metres) apart. Exactly 11 rungs are showing above the water level. The tide rose 8 feet (2.4 metres); how many rungs would now be showing?

See Advanced WALLY Test solution on page 35.

4 Fiendish Puzzles

4.1 The Cellar Door

A little girl was warned by her parents never to open the cellar door or she would see things that she was not meant to see. One day while her parents were out she did open the cellar door. What did she see?

4.2 The Deadly Shot

A man lay dead in a field. Next to him was a gun. One shot had been fired and because of that shot the man had died. Yet he had not been shot. In fact, there was no wound or mark on his body. How had he died?

4.3 Flat Out

A driver whose car had no brakes was approaching a level crossing at 60 miles per hour while a train was approaching the same crossing also at 60 miles per hour. The crossing was unmanned and had no barriers. The train was 100 yards long and it was 50 yards from the crossing. The car was 100 yards from the crossing. Neither train nor car stopped or changed direction or speed. The driver did not get out of his car. How did he survive the crossing?

4.4 An Odd Story

Three men went into a cafe and each had a single cup of coffee. Each put an odd number of lumps of sugar into his cup of coffee. In total they put 12 lumps of sugar in their cups. How many lumps did each consume?

4.5 Free Maps

At some stage between the two world wars, the British government decided that it would be desirable to produce accurate maps of the whole country by using the new technique of aerial photography. They were very concerned that the cost of the project would be high as it involved many flights, much film, and long hours of painstaking matching of photographs. In the end the whole process ended up costing the government nothing. Why not?

4.6   What a Shock I

A man woke up. He lit a match. He saw something and died of shock. What was going on?

4.7   What a Shock II

A man was searching a trunk in the attic when he found something that caused him to drop dead of fright. What did he find?

4.8   The Deadly Party

A man went to a party and drank some of the punch. He then left early. Everyone else at the party who drank the punch subsequently died of poisoning. Why did the man not die?

4.9   Speechless

Two men who were good friends had not seen each other for several years. One afternoon they met but they did not speak to each other. Neither was deaf or dumb and there was no prohibition on speaking in the place where they met. Why did they not speak to each other?

4.10   How to Hug

A boy was about to go on his first date. Since he had never embraced a girl before he was anxious to learn a little about how to do it. He went to his local public library and saw a book entitled *How to Hug*. He took it home to read and was greatly disappointed; it gave him no useful advice at all. Why not?

4.11 The Healthy Dairymaids

In the eighteenth century a disease called smallpox was responsible for the deaths of millions of people world-wide. The man whom we can thank for defeating the scourge of smallpox is Edward Jenner, an English country doctor who lived from 1749 to 1823. He noticed that dairy-maids never caught smallpox. From this observation he went on to develop a treatment to prevent smallpox and thereby became one of the world's most famous doctors. Why did dairymaids never catch smallpox?

4.12 Toothache

A man was suffering from a toothache so he went to a dentist and had two bad teeth removed. The dentist had done a good job and the man was pleased that he was no longer in pain. Some time later, in a court case, judgment was rendered against the man and he was forced to pay damages to a third party because he had had those teeth removed. Why should that have been so? (Incidentally, the dentist was not at fault and was not involved in the court case.)

4.13 The Lake Problem

There is a large irregularly shaped lake on your estate. It is of variable and unknown depth. There are no rivers or streams entering or leaving the lake. How would you find the volume of water in the lake?

4.14 The Realization

A man was walking downstairs in a building when he suddenly realized that his wife had just died. How?

4.15 The Deadly Dish

Two men went into a restaurant. They both ordered the same dish from the menu. After they tasted it one of the men immediately got up from the table, went outside of the restaurant, and shot himself. Why?

4.16 Men in Uniform

Two men are in the back of a van which is parked on a country road. Both men are in uniform. One is dead. The other is angry and frustrated. What happened?

The Advanced WALLY Test Answers

Total up your number of correct answers. Then see how you rate below:

Score	Official Rating
12–15	Smart Alec
7–11	Wally
0–6	Mega Wally

The correct answers are as follows:

(a) *Un garçon.*

(b) Because if they fell forward they would land in the boat!

(c) No. The only way you can have a widow is to be dead.

(d) You would come out near where you started. It is not possible to dig through the earth's molten core.

(e) A L B U M E N

(f) They are a $1 note and a $100 note. (One of them is not a $1 bill; it is the $100 bill.)

(g) The letter ''o'' (or nothing).

(h) There is no such thing as a mommy bull.

(i) His undertaker.

(j) It is very likely. The average number of arms is very slightly less than two, so anyone with two arms has more than the average.

(k) Guilty but in Seine.

(l) Two. One on each side.

(m) All 12 of them.

(n) Pigs cannot say.

(o) Eleven, just as before (the tide also raises the boat).

35

4.17   Healthy People I

In the early twentieth century many healthy people were operated on for medical conditions they did not have. Why?

4.18   Healthy People II

A hospital director recently confirmed that many of the people admitted to his hospital were not ill at all. They were perfectly healthy, yet they were given hospital care and treatment. Why?

4.19   The Grand Prix

A world-famous racing driver was approaching a bend in a formula-one Grand Prix race. Suddenly he braked very sharply and came around the bend to find crashed cars strewn dangerously across the track. He had not been able to see over or around the bend. The officials had not warned him and there was no smoke, fire, smell, or noise that he could have detected. So how did he know that something was wrong in time to avoid danger?

4.20   The Stranger in the Car

A man and his wife were driving quickly from the suburbs into town when their car ran out of fuel. The man left his wife in the car after telling her to keep the windows closed and the doors locked. When he returned, although the doors and windows were still locked and had remained so throughout, he found his wife dead inside and a stranger in the car. The car had not been broken into or damaged in any way, and it had no sun-roof or hatchback; the only means of entry were the doors. How had the wife died and who was the stranger?

4.21   Eggshell Finish

Why was the man painting his portrait on an eggshell?

THE CLUES

1 Easy Puzzles

1.1 The Apple Problem

Q: Were any of the apples split or eaten?
A: No.

Q: Did each of the six girls get one apple?
A: Yes.

Q: Were there only six girls and no other people in the room?
A: Yes.

Q: Were there only six apples in the room both at the beginning and end of the process?
A: Yes.

Q: Did any girl get more than one apple?
A: Yes.

1.2 The Two Presidents

Q: Were they brother and sister?
A: No. (There has not yet been a woman president.)

Q: Were they both elected through the normal electoral process?
A: Yes.

Q: Were they both men?
A: Yes.

1.3 Game, Set, and Match

Q: Were they playing standard regulation tennis?
A: Yes.

Q: Were they both physically normal?
A: Yes.

Q: Were they playing on the same court at the same time?
A: Yes.

1.4 Wondrous Walk

Q: Was it a very short distance that he walked?
A: No. He walked from Dublin to Cork and that is nearly two hundred miles.

Q: Are there many pubs on the road from Dublin to Cork?
A: Yes.

Q: Did he take a particular route to avoid the pubs?
A: No.

Q: Did he use special roads such as turnpikes, highways, tunnels, newly constructed roads, etc.?
A: No. He used the normal roads.

Q: Did it take him a long time to complete the journey?
A: Yes, very.

1.5 Father and Son

It is impossible for a father to be younger than his son. However, it is possible to have a grandfather who is younger than your father. Alternatively, you could have a grandmother younger than your mother. However, it is not possible to have a grandfather *and* grandmother younger than your father and mother. Confused? Keep thinking!

1.6 The Amazing Fall

Q: Did he wear any special clothing or glider wings?
A: No.

Q: Was he a normal man?
A: Yes.

Q: Did he come in contact with anything on the way down which slowed his fall?
A: No. He fell from the plane to the ground and accelerated all the way.

Q: How high was the plane?
A: It was 5,000 feet above sea level (but it was not flying over the sea).

Q: Was the plane flying fast?
A: No.

1.7 Shopping Is Good for You

Q: Did he need to buy some drug or medication?
A: No.

Q: Was he fully conscious and awake when he crashed the plane?
A: Yes.

Q: Did he deliberately ignore his tutor's instructions?
A: No.

Q: Did he deliberately crash the plane?
A: No.

Q: Did he have some kind of ailment or disability?
A: Yes.

1.8 Your Turn to Drive

Q: Were both brothers able and licensed to drive?
A: Yes.

Q: Did one always drive in Birmingham and the other in London?
A: Yes.

Q: Was this through choice or necessity?
A: Necessity, they did not like this.

Q: When one drove was his brother a passenger?
A: Yes.

Q: Do their jobs have any relevance?
A: No.

Q: Do the cities have relevance?
A: Yes.

Q: Were the brothers normal in every way?
A: No.

1.9 See Saw

There is no hidden catch in this. What is the easiest and most direct way for this man to communicate his request?

1.10 The Two Lookouts

Q: Were the two lookouts facing in opposite directions?
A: Yes.

Q: Were any mirrors, lenses, or cameras involved?
A: No.

Q: Could each see the other's face?
A: Yes.

1.11 The Deadly Drive

Q: Was anything mechanical or electrical in his car tampered with?
A: No.

Q: Was his death an accident?
A: Yes.

Q: Was something stolen which could have prevented this accident?
A: Yes.

Q: Was it something he used while driving?
A: Yes.

1.12 Another Man in an Elevator

Q: Is he completely capable of operating the elevator?
A: Yes.

Q: If he wanted to go up to his room at some other time of day would he use the elevator?
A: Yes.

Q: Do other guests use the elevator to ascend in the evening?
A: Yes.

Q: Is the man physically normal?
A: Yes.

Q: Is he alone on his journey at eight every evening?
A: No.

Q: Does this regular evening journey serve a useful purpose?
A: Yes.

1.13 Growing Younger

Q: Was Ben a normal human being?
A: Yes.

Q: Was he born on February 29?
A: No.

Q: As each year went by did he get one year older?
A: Yes.

Q: Does it have something to do with the dates?
A: Yes.

1.14 The Habitual Walker

Q: Was the train a special train of some kind?
A: No. It was the regular train.

Q: Was the train early?
A: No.

Q: Is his deafness relevant?
A: Yes, but only because he could not hear train coming.

Q: Had his clock stopped?
A: No, he had three clocks and wound them all the night before. They all kept good time.

Q: Was there something special about that particular day which threw out his schedule?
A: Yes.

1.15 Greenland

Q: Was the country green when he discovered it?
A: No.

Q: Did he believe that it would or could become green?
A: No.

Q: Did he name it after some person or place?
A: No.

Q: Was the name given meant to be descriptive?
A: Yes.

Q: Was the name in any way accurate?
A: No.

1.16 Radio On

Q: Did the girl influence or direct the radio in any way?
A: No.

Q: Did everyone listening to that station at the time suffer the same loss of reception?
A: No. Most did not but a small number did.

Q: Was it anything to do with her location?
A: Yes.

Q: Is this a rare or a common occurrence?
A: Common.

1.17   The Boxing Match

Q: Did one boxer kick or butt the other boxer, or hit him with some implement?
A: No.

Q: Was everything about the fight legal and proper?
A: Yes.

Q: And yet no punches were thrown?
A: No man threw a punch.

Q: Was there something unusual about the two boxers?
A: Yes.

1.18   The Nephew

There is no catch to this one. The man and woman were a normal brother and sister. The boy was the man's nephew but he was not the woman's nephew. There is a very simple explanation.

1.19   Barrel Trouble

When he started, the barrel was empty. He then filled it with something. That something was not a light gas nor was it anything lighter than air. There are no vacuums or tricky physics involved. Anyone could do this!

1.20   Rival Fans

Q: Did they know each other?
A: No.

Q: Was the Argentinian fan grateful to the man who had struck him?
A: Yes.

Q: Did the Brazilian fan help his rival in some way?
A: Yes.

1.21 Coming Up for Air

Q: Could she get a valid sample by simply taking the lid off the jar and shaking it around?
A: No. How could she be sure that she had removed all the original air?

Q: Did she use some kind of machine to create a vacuum?
A: No.

Q: Does the solution involve advanced physics or complicated devices?
A: No. She used a very simple idea.

1.22 Nuts Away!

Q: Did the boy suggest a way of attaching the wheel?
A: Yes.

Q: Did it involve retrieving the lost nuts?
A: No.

Q: Did it involve any equipment not normally available in a car?
A: No.

Q: Was it a sensible idea which was easy to implement?
A: Yes.

1.23 The Golf Pro

Q: Does this have anything to do with a left-hander's golf clubs or equipment or methods?
A: No.

Q: Is it because left-handed players make better teachers?
A: Yes. Why?

1.24 Deduction

Q: Did the man find the name and address written down somewhere?

A: No.

Q: Did he follow his wife or have her followed?
A: No.

Q: Did he find some article giving a clue to the lover's identity?

A: No.

Q: Was he expecting to find her on his return?
A: No. He thought that she would arrange to meet her lover.

2 Moderate Puzzles

2.1 The Penny Black

Q: Was the paper or the ink of the Penny Black defective in any way?

A: No.

Q: Did the design change when the Penny Red was introduced?

A: No, only the color.

Q: Was there a problem with the Penny Black because it was black?

A: Yes.

Q: Did the problem have to do with the printing or copying?

A: No.

2.2 Flat Tire I

Q: Did he drive all those miles with a flat tire?
A: Yes.

Q: Did it make steering or braking or balancing the car more difficult?
A: No.

Q: Did he do something to the flat tire or to any of the other tires or wheels?
A: No.

Q: Did he drive on the wheel rim?
A: No.

Q: Did he have a special car or special skill?
A: No. Anyone could do this in any car.

2.3 Flat Tire II

The instructor could not tell from their clothing or the weather or any other external factor whether they were telling the truth. The tardy students had in fact arrived by car but had suffered no puncture or flat tire. The lecturer asked them one question which exposed their deceit. What was the question?

2.4 Bottled Fruit

This is not only physically possible; it is often done. There are producers who sell a fully grown pear inside each bottle of pear liqueur. The mouth of the bottle is much smaller than the pear, yet they get the pear into the bottle without any special implements or aids and they do not form the bottle around the pear. How do they do it?

2.5 The Cowboy's Fate

Q: Was this cause of death accidental?
A: Yes.

Q: Did it involve firearms?
A: No.

Q: Did it involve other people?
A: No.

Q: Did it involve animals?
A: Yes.

Q: Did these animals attack them?
A: No.

2.6 The Village Idiot

Q: Was the village idiot simply an idiot?
A: No.

Q: Was there a good reason for him to always choose the coin rather than the bill?
A: Yes.

Q: Was getting the money in coin in some way more valuable or useful to him than having a bill would be?
A: No.

2.7 The Island Fire

Q: Does the solution involve him going into the sea or using sea water?

A: No. There were steep cliffs plunging into shark-infested seas!

Q: Does he have time to cut a fire-break?
A: No.

Q: Can he use something to put out the fire?
A: No.

Q: Does he stay on the island the whole time?
A: Yes.

Q: Is the strong wind relevant?
A: Yes.

2.8 The Sleepy Kings

Q: Were the two kings related in any way?
A: No.

Q: Were the kings both physically normal?
A: Yes.

Q: Did these events happen about the same time?
A: No. King George II's "long sleep" took place in 1752, some 170 years after the similar episode for King Henry III.

Q: Were they suffering from some illness or using some kind of drug?
A: No.

Q: Did it matter that they were kings?
A: No.

Q: Was this a normal occurrence at that time?
A: Yes.

2.9 The Portrait

Do not make any assumptions here. Work through the statements logically. Start at the end—if he has no brothers then who can "my father's son" be?

2.10 Winning Isn't Everything

Q: Is there some trick about stroke play/match play or not finishing particular games?
A: No.

Q: Is there something particular to golf or could they have played any sport where they finish 1, 2, 3?
A: Any sport.

Q: Were they correct in their calculations?
A: Yes.

Q: Did each of them win about the same number of games?
A: Yes.

2.11 The Reluctant Diner

Q: Was he trying to lose weight?
A: No.

Q: Had he planned to eat with someone else?
A: No.

Q: Was he able to eat before 8 P.M.?
A: Yes.

Q: Is there a medical or social reason for his reluctance to eat?
A: No.

Q: Was he thirsty and did he drink before 8 P.M.?
A: He was thirsty but he did not drink.

(BONUS CLUE: The next evening he did the same thing but waited until two minutes past eight before eating and drinking.)

2.12 Death in a Car

Q: Was his death murder or suicide?
A: No, it was an accident.

Q: Was he or the car unusual in any way?
A: No.

Q: Did he know he was going to die?
A: Yes, but only just before he died.

Q: Was the car in a moving accident?
A: No. It was stationary immediately before, during, and after his death.

Q: Was there any wound or mark on his body?
A: No.

Q: Was any other person or animal involved?
A: No.

Q: Was the location where he parked the car critical?
A: Yes.

2.13 Last Cord

Q: Was he strangled by the cord?
A: No.

Q: Was his death an accident?
A: Yes.

Q: Did any other human or animal cause his death?
A: No.

Q: Was his death violent?
A: Yes.

Q: Was it a special kind of cord?
A: Yes, and it was broken.

2.14 Saturday Flights

Q: Does it involve time zones or calendar changes?
A: No.

Q: Did he spend just 4 nights and 5 days in Los Angeles?
A: Yes.

Q: Did he arrive and leave by plane?
A: Yes.

Q: Was it a scheduled flight or a private plane?
A: A private plane.

2.15   The Trains That Did Not Crash

Q: Did each train run from one end of the tunnel through and out the opposite end?
A: Yes.

Q: Did both trains run on the same single track but in opposite directions?
A: Yes.

Q: Were they normal, full-sized trains?
A: Yes.

Q: Did they somehow pass by each other in the tunnel?
A: No.

2.16   Copyright

It is impossible to have a copyright restriction on the words of the English language or the shape of the continents of the world. But it is possible to copyright specific expressions of these concepts, as in a proprietary dictionary or atlas. How would you know if someone had copied your specific list of words or representation of the world and claimed it to be an original work? How could you prove the person had copied your expression rather than come up with the work independently?

2.17   The Ransom

Q: Did the man receive a phone call at the phone booth?
A: No.

52

Q: Was the kidnapper in the park?
A: No.

Q: Did the kidnapper get the diamond safely out of the park?
A: Yes.

Q: Was any other person involved?
A: No.

Q: Did the diamond leave the park in some sort of vehicle or through a tunnel?
A: No.

2.18   Moving Parts

Q: Do both objects serve a common and useful function?
A: Yes.

Q: Does either of them use electricity?
A: No.

Q: Are the thousands of moving parts man-made?
A: No.

Q: Are the objects recent inventions?
A: No. They have both been around in one form or another for centuries.

Q: Are they in common use indoors?
A: The one with thousands of parts is commonly found indoors. The other is not in such common use and is found outdoors.

2.19   An Early Burial

Q: Was he buried the same week of the same year?
A: Yes.

Q: Was he buried the day before he died?
A: Yes.

Q: Was he dead when he was buried?
A: Yes.

Q: Does where he died and was buried have anything to do with it?
A: Yes.

Q: Could this happen in, say, New York or London?
A: No.

2.20 Trouble and Strife

Q: Was she angry because of who called or what the caller said?
A: No.

Q: Did either of them know the caller?
A: No.

Q: Was she angry because of what her husband said?
A: Yes.

Q: Did he hold a long conversation with the caller?
A: No. He answered the phone in the normal way and replaced the receiver when he learned that it was a wrong number.

Q: Did she have good reason to be upset?
A: Yes.

Q: If she had not been knitting would she have been angry?
A: No.

2.21 Bath Water

Q: Was the maid heating water on the stove in order to add all of it to the bath water?
A: Yes.

Q: Was the temperature in the house steady?
A: Yes.

Q: Was there anything unusual about the kitchen, the stove, the water, or the bathtub?
A: No.

Q: Was the water very hot?
A: Yes. It was steaming.

2.22 The Hold-Up

Q: Were the people whom the man held up angry?
A: Yes.

Q: Was the policeman an accomplice?
A: No. He was a regular policeman.

Q: Did he know the man?
A: No.

Q: Did the policeman clearly see and understand the man's wrongdoing?
A: Yes.

Q: Did the policeman try to take back the $200?
A: Certainly not! But he did tell the man not to hold up people again.

2.23 The Worst Sailor

Q: Did Jim have some special skill or attribute useful to the captain?
A: No.

Q: Did he perform some other tasks?
A: No. He was just one of the sailors.

Q: Was he less expensive to pay or keep than the other sailors?
A: No.

Q: Was the ship a real ship at sea?
A: Yes.

2.24 The Valuable Book

Q: Did he destroy the book because it contained something damaging or threatening to him or his family?
A: No.

Q: Was he hoping to collect the insurance?
A: No.

Q: Does this involve fraud, blackmail, or robbery?
A: No.

Q: Was he breaking the law by burning this book?
A: No.

Q: Did he do it for personal gain?
A: Yes.

3   Difficult Puzzles

3.1   Cuddly Bears

Q: Did the hospital lock up or guard the bears?
A: No.

Q: Did they make them deliberately unattractive to the children?
A: No.

Q: Did they threaten or penalize the children or their parents?
A: No.

Q: Did they play on the children's love and concern for the bears?

3.2   The High-Society Dinner

Q: Was the man a thief or the thief's accomplice?
A: No.

Q: Did he have a coin in his pocket?
A: No.

Q: Was he an aristocrat like the other guests?
A: Yes.

Q: Was he afraid of showing what was in his pockets?
A: Yes.

Q: Would it show that he was a criminal?
A: No.

Q: Had he taken something?
A: Yes.

3.3   Eight Years Old

Q: Was the girl physically normal?
A: Yes.

Q: Were her eight years normal earth years of twelve months each?
A: Yes.

Q: Was she sixteen on her second birthday?
A: No.

Q: Was she nine on her second birthday?
A: No.

Q: Could she have been born this century?
A: No. Though she did live this century.

Q: Was she unique in being eight years old on her first birthday?
A: No. It happened to everyone else born when she was born.

3.4 Cover That Hole

Q: Was it something peculiar to the town?
A: No. It would be a good idea anywhere.

Q: Does it have to do with cost or efficiency?
A: No.

Q: Does it have to do with safety?
A: Yes.

Q: Are manhole covers the same shape but slightly larger than the manhole rims?
A: Yes.

3.5 The Protagoras Paradox

In approaching the trial each man felt that he had an excellent chance of winning. The young man argued that if he won his case the court would have cleared him of any obligation to pay. If he lost the case he would still not have won his first case and would therefore still be free of the obligations of the original contract.

Protagoras believed that if he won the case, it meant by definition that the court had found in his favor against his former pupil, who would therefore have to pay him any specified damages, i.e., the tuition fees. On the other hand if he lost his case, then his opponent, the pupil, would have won his first case and would therefore be contractually bound to pay.

3.6 Hand in Glove

Q: Did the glove manufacturer smuggle the gloves into the country?
A: No! He was a reputable businessman.

Q: Did he disguise them as something else?
A: No.

Q: Did he pay any duty?
A: No.

Q: Are your goods impounded if you refuse to pay duty?
A: Yes, the goods are then sold at auction to the highest bidder. (The value of the sets of gloves at auction would be higher than the duty.)

3.7 The School Superintendent

Q: Did the superintendent ask plenty of questions?
A: Yes.

Q: Did all the children raise their hands?
A: Yes.

Q: Did the teacher always pick a child who knew the answer?
A: Yes.

Q: Were they normal children?
A: Yes.

Q: Did all the children know all the answers?
A: No.

Q: Did the teacher know the questions in advance?
A: No.

3.8 No Trumps

There are four separate hands at bridge; each with 13 cards. The 13 trumps are randomly distributed between the four hands. It would be terrific if you and your partner had all 13 trumps as you would be bound to win at least seven tricks. It is unlikely that you would have all 13 trumps; but is it even more unlikely that you will have none between you?

3.9 How to Beat Nick Faldo

Q: Did they play a game of golf on a proper golf course?
A: Yes.

Q: Was the challenger also a world-class player?
A: No. He was a good player.

Q: Did the champion play his best?
A: Yes.

Q: Did the timing of the match give the challenger his advantage?
A: Yes.

3.10 How to Beat Carl Lewis

Q: Did they run a race?
A: Yes.

Q: Was the time they ran the race important?
A: No.

Q: Did they run backwards, sideways, or on their hands?
A: No.

Q: Was it a long-distance race?
A: No, it covered a short distance.

3.11 The Missing Furniture

Q: Did he fall to his death?
A: No.

Q: Was his death an accident?
A: Yes.

Q: Was the piece of furniture heavy or unusual?
A: No. It was a very common piece of furniture.

Q: Was his job unusual and dangerous?
A: Yes.

3.12 The Dead Man

Q: Was the cord attached to anything else in the room before or during his death?
A: No.

Q: Was any ice involved?
A: No. (What an odd question!)

Q: Was his death a suicide?
A: Yes.

Q: Was any other person or thing involved?
A: No.

3.13 The Busy Hospital

Q: Did people drive faster or more dangerously because they wore seat belts?
A: No.

Q: Was there an increase in injuries to pedestrians, cyclists, or other road users?
A: No, but there were more injured drivers and passengers.

Q: Was the seriousness of the injuries generally reduced?
A: Yes.

Q: Was there something peculiar about this town, its inhabitants, or the hospital?
A: No.

Q: Was the wearing of seat belts successful in its aim of improving road safety?
A: Yes.

3.14   The Fallen Sign

Q: Could the man see the correct position by matching the broken parts of the post or the post with the hole in the ground?
A: No.

Q: Did he use the sun, stars, wind, or a landmark as a guide?
A: No.

Q: Did he use some piece of knowledge to replace the sign correctly in the ground?
A: Yes.

Q: Could anyone have done this or did he have some special skill or knowledge?
A: Anyone could have done it.

3.15   False Fingerprints

Q: Did the man use his wife's fingerprints?
A: No.

Q: Had he brought in a set of false fingerprints especially for this purpose?
A: No. He thought of doing it on the spur of the moment.

Q: Did he have some particular skill or knowledge of science to plant the false prints?
A: No.

Q: Did he use something easily available?
A: Yes.

Q: Did it fool the police?
A: Yes.

Q: Did he leave a proper set of fingerprints on the murder weapon?
A: No.

3.16 Found, Lost, Found

Q: Did the man deliberately throw away something which he valued?
A: Yes.

Q: Was he pleased to throw it away?
A: Yes.

Q: Was he later pleased to get it back?
A: Yes.

Q: Did he simply change his mind?
A: No. The circumstances changed.

Q: When he threw it away, did it represent a danger?
A: Yes.

Q: Did it present a danger when he got it back?
A: No.

3.17 The Crippled Child

Q: Did the parents believe that the child would eventually be cured?
A: No, they understood it was permanently disabled.

Q: Were they sadistic or malevolent in some way?
A: No.

Q: Was the child's handicap of some use to them?
A: Yes, quite beneficial in fact.

Q: Does this usefulness involve medical research or religion?
A: No.

3.18 Insurance

Q: Was this an unusual ambition?
A: No. Many people share this personal goal.

Q: Would achieving this goal injure or kill him?
A: No.

Q: Was it a dangerous undertaking to him or to others?
A: No.

Q: Was it something which would prove costly?
A: Yes.

Q: Is it something which involves skill or luck?
A: Yes, both.

3.19 Eggs

The reason has to do with a practical advantage for the survival of the birds. It is based on a simple physical consequence of the shape. It has nothing to do with the act of egg laying.

3.20 The Guard Dog

Q: Did the boy enter the orchard while the dog was there?
A: Yes.

Q: Did he drug the dog or trap it?
A: No. It remained free to move around.

Q: Did he give it food?
A: No.

Q: Did he distract it in some way?
A: Yes.

3.21 The Last Message

Q: Had the man been murdered and the scene made to look like suicide?
A: Yes.

Q: Was there something about the room or the desk or the gun which indicated to the detective that it was murder?
A: No.

Q: Was the clue in the cassette recording?
A: Yes.

Q: Did it have to do with the man's voice or accent?
A: No.

3.22 The Japanese Speaker

Q: Was it the fact that an American was speaking Japanese which amused them?
A: No.

Q: Was it the subject matter?
A: No.

Q: Was it the way he spoke?
A: Yes.

Q: Was it his American accent or his grammar?
A: No.

Q: Was he taught by a good Japanese speaker?
A: Yes. He was taught by his wife, who was Japanese.

4 Fiendish Puzzles

4.1 The Cellar Door

Q: Did the little girl see something which amazed or surprised her?
A: Yes.

Q: Would it amaze or surprise most people?
A: No.

Q: Was something unusual kept in the cellar?
A: Yes.

Q: Is this what she saw?
A: No.

Q: Did she see a living creature?
A: No.

4.2   The Deadly Shot

Q: Does it matter what the man shot at?
A: No.

Q: Did he hit what he shot at?
A: Irrelevant.

Q: Was any other human or animal involved in his death?
A: No.

Q: Did something fall on him out of the sky?
A: No.

Q: Did he know he was going to die before he died?
A: Yes.

Q: Did he know he was going to die before he fired the gun?
A: No.

4.3   Flat Out

Q: Were the road and railway track at right angles to each other and did they cross on the same ground?
A: Yes.

Q: Did the driver go over a bridge or under a tunnel?
A: No.

Q: Did the car, the driver, and the train all get across the level crossing intact?
A: Yes.

Q: Were the car and the train on the level crossing at the exact same instant?
A: Yes.

4.4 An Odd Story

This puzzle does not involve putting one cup inside another cup or transferring coffee or sugar from one cup to another. Nor does it involve one man drinking another man's coffee. How could each man put an odd number of lumps in his drink yet exactly 12 lumps (an even number) were used altogether?

4.5 Free Maps

Q: Did the British government sell the maps to cover the costs?
A: No.

Q: Did they get the use of the planes, photographers, and other needs free?
A: No.

Q: Were the maps produced accurate?
A: Yes.

Q: Did they reveal useful or unexpected information?
A: Yes.

Q: Did the government sell this information?
A: No.

Q: Did they raise money because they now had this information?
A: Yes.

4.6 What a Shock I

Q: Did the man see something or someone?
A: Someone.

Q: Was the person he saw alive?
A: No.

Q: Did he expect to see someone else?
A: Yes.

Q: Did he now know that he would soon die?
A: Yes.

4.7   What a Shock II

Q: Did the man see a dead human or animal?
A: No.

Q: Did he see objects which terrified him?
A: Yes.

Q: What were they?
A: Glass eyes!

Q: Did seeing them make him realize that he would soon die?
A: Yes.

4.8   The Deadly Party

Q: Did the man poison the other people?
A: No.

Q: Did anybody add anything to the punch after he left?
A: No.

Q: Was there something wrong with the glasses, ladle, or the punch bowl itself?
A: No.

Q: Were all the people physically normal?
A: Yes.

Q: Was there a relationship between the people, or between them and the man who left early, that matters here?
A: No.

Q: Was there something special about him which made him immune to the poison?

A: No. It could have been anyone, provided they left early.

4.9 Speechless

Q: Did the two friends recognize and greet each other?
A: Yes.

Q: Were they close to each other?
A: Yes.

Q: Were they being watched or supervised?
A: No.

Q: Were they afraid of being overheard?
A: No.

Q: Could other people there speak?
A: No.

Q: Was it indoors?
A: No.

4.10   How to Hug

Q: Was the book about hugging or embracing?
A: No.

Q: Did it have the wrong cover or a misprinted cover?
A: No.

Q: Was it a genuine non-fiction book written in English?
A: Yes.

Q: Was the boy physically normal and could he read?
A: Yes.

Q: Was the title of the book an accurate description of its contents?
A: Yes.

Q: Would one recognize this type of book if one saw it?
A: Yes.

4.11   The Healthy Dairymaids

Q: Were other sections of the community immune from smallpox or was it just dairymaids?
A: Just dairymaids.

Q: Was it something to do with drinking milk or eating dairy produce?
A: No.

Q: Was it because of the way the dairymaids milked the cows?
A: No.

Q: Did they gain an immunity because they worked closely with cows?
A: Yes.

Q: Were they immune because they had previously caught smallpox?
A: No.

4.12   Toothache

This story is based on fact. It happened to a man in Sweden at around the turn of the century. It is extremely unlikely that it could happen nowadays. The man had been poor but at the time of the trial he was wealthy. He was physically and mentally normal, and was not a criminal. The teeth he had had removed were normal human teeth with no particular value. However, he was judged to have injured the interests of a third party by having those teeth out. Why?

4.13   The Lake Problem

Q: Does the solution involve measuring the height of the water in the lake?
A: No.

Q: Does the solution involve measuring the temperature of the lake?
A: No.

Q: Is the solution a practical and realistic way of estimating the volume of water in the lake?
A: Yes.

Q: Does the solution involve taking samples of water from the lake?
A: Yes.

4.14   The Realization

Q: Had the man's wife died?
A: Yes.

Q: Was it murder, an accident, or suicide?
A: It was an accident.

Q: Was she in the same building as he was?
A: Yes, but she was on another floor—well outside his sight and hearing range.

Q: Did he hear something?
A: No.

Q: Did he see something which caused him to realize she had died?
A: Yes.

Q: Was it something major like a fire or explosion which killed her?
A: No. Other people near her did not die.

4.15 The Deadly Dish

Q: Was the dish poisoned or distasteful in some way?
A: It was not poisoned. It was not distasteful to anyone but him.

Q: Did tasting the dish cause him to deliberately commit suicide?
A: Yes.

Q: Did he recognize the taste?
A: No, but that was the reason that he shot himself.

Q: Was the dish human flesh, or the flesh of a pet or an endangered species?
A: No. It was the meat of a bird.

Q: Was there something in his earlier life which was linked to his recognizing or not recognizing the taste?
A: Yes.

4.16 Men in Uniform

Q: Were the two men both wearing the same uniform?
A: No.

Q: Had the angry man killed the other man?
A: Yes.

Q: Was it an accident or a case of mistaken identity?
A: No.

Q: Was something preventing the murderer from leaving the scene?
A: Yes.

4.17 Healthy People I

Q: Did this actually happen?
A: Yes.

Q: Were the people unusual in any way? Were they of one particular race or type or sex?
A: No.

Q: Were their operations genuine mistakes on the part of the medical community?
A: Yes.

Q: Were they wrongly diagnosed because of the use of some new technology or medical method?
A: Yes.

Q: Is it a technology or method which is in common use today?
A: Yes.

4.18 Healthy People II

Q: Is this occurrence unusual?
A: No. It is common.

Q: Are these people mentally ill or socially deprived?
A: No.

Q: Does their physical state require hospital treatment?
A: Strictly speaking, no, but it is usual and beneficial.

4.19 The Grand Prix

Q: Was there a car ahead of him which swerved?
A: No.

Q: Did he know for sure there was a crash around the bend?
A: No, but he knew that something was happening there.

Q: Did he see something which alerted him?
A: Yes.

Q: Was it a deliberate signal from someone or something?
A: No.

4.20   The Stranger in the Car

Q: Was there something special or unusual about the car?
A: No. It was a regular four-door family car.

Q: Was the stranger a human being? Which sex?
A: Yes. Male.

Q: Was the woman's death murder or suicide?
A: No. It was accidental.

Q: Did she die of poisoning, suffocation, or heart attack?
A: No.

Q: Was the stranger the cause of the woman's death?
A: Yes, although not deliberately.

4.21   Eggshell Finish

Q: Was the man a serious painter?
A: No.

Q: Was he painting his likeness on the eggshell for fun?
A: No, he had a very good reason.

Q: Does his profession matter?
A: Yes.

Q: Did the portrait really look like him?
A: Yes, when he was working.

THE ANSWERS

1 Easy Puzzles

1.1 The Apple Problem

The first five girls each took an apple. The sixth girl took the basket as well as the apple in it.

1.2 The Two Presidents

They were the same man. Grover Cleveland (1837–1908) served two terms as president of the United States, but the terms were not consecutive. He was president from 1885 to 1889 and from 1893 to 1897.

1.3 Game, Set, and Match

The two men were partners playing doubles.

1.4 Wondrous Walk

The man did not pass a single pub because he went into every one!

1.5 Father and Son

Let's say that William's father was 60, his mother was 25, and his mother's father was 45. Because everyone has two grandfathers, it is quite possible for a maternal grandfather to be younger than one's father.

1.6 The Amazing Fall

The plane was parked on the runway.

1.7 Shopping Is Good for You

The man had neglected to buy a new battery for his hearing aid. The old battery failed just as he was coming in to land and he therefore did not hear his tutor's crucial instructions.

1.8 Your Turn to Drive

The brothers were Siamese twins, joined at the side. They lived in Birmingham, Alabama. Because they drove on the right-hand side of the road the steering wheel was on the left-hand side of the car. The brother who sat on the left always drove. When they were in London, England, the other drove because the steering wheel was on the right-hand side of the car.

1.9 See Saw

The deaf man says to the storekeeper, "I would like to buy a saw, please."

1.10 The Two Lookouts

Although the guards were looking in opposite directions, they were not back to back. They were facing each other.

1.11 The Deadly Drive

The man's expensive designer sunglasses were stolen. He normally wore them while driving. As he came around a bend in the mountain, he was blinded by the evening sun and ran off the road.

1.12 Another Man in an Elevator

Bill was on holiday with his wife and two-year-old son. The boy is a very lively fellow. Bill and his wife found that the best way to tire the youngster out each night was to let him climb five flights of stairs just before his bedtime. He enjoyed doing it but for Bill it was a chore.

1.13 Growing Younger

Ben was born in the year 2000 B.C. So in 1985 B.C. he was 15 and in 1980 B.C. he was 20.

1.14 The Habitual Walker

On that particular morning all the clocks were due to be moved forward for the summer. Although he had wound all his clocks he had neglected to put them forward one hour. Consequently, when he set out thinking it was 7:45 A.M. it was really 8:45 A.M. He was hit by the 9 o'clock train.

1.15 Greenland

In about 982 a Norseman, Eric the Red, discovered Greenland. He wanted to encourage people to settle there so he called it Greenland to make it sound attractive. It is a very early example of deliberately misleading labelling!

1.16 Radio On

The girl was listening to the radio in her father's car. He drove through a tunnel and reception was temporarily interrupted.

1.17 The Boxing Match

No man threw a punch because the boxing match was between two women boxers.

1.18 The Nephew

The boy was the woman's son, and therefore he was her brother's nephew.

1.19 Barrel Trouble

The man filled the barrel with holes! Since there was now less barrel it weighed less.

1.20 Rival Fans

The two men were in a restaurant. The Argentinian fan had a fishbone stuck in his throat and was choking. The other man was quick-witted enough to give him a strong blow on the back, thereby dislodging the bone and saving his life.

1.21 Coming Up for Air

The girl filled the jar with water at the school. When she reached the appropriate point at the city center she poured all the water out. What replaced it was a true sample of the surrounding air.

1.22 Nuts Away!

The boy suggested that the man take one wheel nut off each of the other three wheels in order to attach the fourth wheel. Once he had done this, the man could safely drive to the nearest garage with each wheel firmly attached by three nuts.

1.23 The Golf Pro

One of the most important tasks for the golf club professional is giving lessons. Most players are right-handed. They can stand opposite a left-handed teacher and watch and copy him more easily. It is just like looking in a mirror, so it makes learning the correct style of swing easier.

1.24 Deduction

He reasoned that she would have called her lover so he simply pressed the redial button on their telephone. When the man answered with his name the husband told him that he had won a prize draw and asked for the address to which it should be sent.

2 Moderate Puzzles

2.1 The Penny Black

The postmark used at that time was always black. It was therefore difficult to tell whether a stamp had been franked or not. This led to people reusing used stamps. On a Penny Red the black postmark was clearly visible.

2.2 Flat Tire I

The flat tire was on the man's spare wheel which he kept in the car trunk. The four wheels he drove on all had properly inflated tires.

2.3 Flat Tire II

The lecturer separated the four students, so that they were not together in the room, and asked each to write down which of the four wheels of the car had suffered the puncture. Of course they did not all say the same wheel. (The chances of them all picking the same wheel are 1 in $4 \times 4 \times 4$; i.e., 1 in 64.)

2.4 Bottled Fruit

The fruit is grown in the bottle. The bottle is tied onto the branch shortly after the fruit starts to form.

2.5 The Cowboy's Fate

The most common cause of death among cowboys was from being dragged along by a galloping horse when the cowboy's foot was caught in a stirrup. This would occur during a fall or when mounting or dismounting.

2.6 The Village Idiot

The so-called village idiot was smart enough to realize that as long as he kept choosing the 50-cent piece, people would keep offering him the choice. If he once took the $5 bill, the stream of coins would stop rolling in.

80

2.7 The Island Fire

The man should set fire to the ground beneath him and walk towards the main fire. The wind will fan the fire he started so as to burn out the end of the island towards which the wind is blowing. He can then walk back to a piece of burnt land and stand there safely when the main fire reaches his end of the island.

2.8 The Sleepy Kings

The kings each slept one night only. The calendar changed in France in 1582 and in England in 1752. Previously the Julian Calendar had been used, but this had allowed a cumulative error to occur which needed to be corrected. Pope Gregory XIII ordered ten days to be dropped from the year 1582. This order was followed by Catholic countries such as France but not by Protestant ones such as England. England eventually adopted the improved Gregorian Calendar in 1752, though by that time the adjustment needed had grown to 11 days.

Incidentally, the thirteen American colonies were under British control so they also changed from Julian to Gregorian calendars in 1752. George Washington was born on February 11, 1732, but after 1752 his birthday became February 22, which is now officially Washington's Birthday.

2.9 The Portrait

The portrait is of the man's daughter.

2.10 Winning Isn't Everything

One third of the games finished A, B, C; one third finished B, C, A, and the other third finished C, A, B. So Alf finished ahead of Bert twice as often as behind him and the same is true for Bert over Chris and Chris over Alf.

2.11 The Reluctant Diner

The businessman was a Muslim. He therefore observed the religious fast for the month of Ramadan. During this period Muslims are not allowed to drink, eat, or smoke between sunrise and sunset.

2.12 Death in a Car

The man drove his car to the beach to watch the sunset over the waves. He fell asleep. The tide came in and seeped in around the car doors and windows. He awoke, but with the pressure of the water, he couldn't get out of the car. The water filled the car and drowned him. Later the tide went out and he was found dead in an empty car.

2.13 Last Cord

Incredible as it may seem, some people enjoy leaping off high buildings or bridges with a length of elastic cord fastened to them. This pastime is known as bungee jumping. The poor man in this situation died when he jumped from a high crane in the field and his bungee cord broke.

2.14 Saturday Flights

Saturday was the name of the man's private plane.

2.15 The Trains That Did Not Crash

One train went through the tunnel in the early afternoon and the other went through in the late afternoon.

2.16 Copyright

Publishers normally include a nonexistent word or a non-existent island in a dictionary or atlas, respectively. If it then appears in somebody else's work, they have clear evidence of copying.

2.17 The Ransom

This is a true story from Taiwan. When the rich man reached the phone booth he found a carrier pigeon in a cage. It had a message attached telling the man to put the diamond in a small bag which was around the pigeon's neck and to release the bird. When the man did this the police were powerless to follow the bird as it returned across the city to its owner.

2.18 Moving Parts

The two objects are an hourglass (often used in the kitchen as an egg-timer) and a sundial.

2.19 An Early Burial

John Brown lived on a Pacific island close to the International Date Line. When you cross the International Date Line (eastwards), your calendar goes back one day. He died on Thursday, December 6, and was flown home that same day for burial. Because the plane flew eastwards over the International Date Line it was Wednesday, December 5, when he was buried later that day. (This could happen if the plane flew, for example, from Fiji to Western Samoa.)

2.20 Trouble and Strife

Mrs. White had been counting her stitches very carefully; the number was well past 300. When Mr. White answered the phone he told the caller their phone number, 837-9263. Hearing this caused Mrs. White to lose count.

2.21 Bath Water

The water in the pan was already boiling when the butler came in. The longer the maid now heated the water the less of it there would be (because of the steam) to heat the tub and the water's temperature would not rise any further.

2.22 The Hold-Up

When the man parked his car outside the bank he held up twenty-five people who were stuck in traffic behind him. The policeman told him not to park like that again.

2.23   The Worst Sailor

The captain would prefer to have ten men like Jim because currently he has fifty men like Jim. He considers almost the entire crew as useless, but is stuck with them for the duration of the voyage!

2.24   The Valuable Book

The man actually owned two copies of the valuable book. By destroying one copy he increased the value of the other.

3   Difficult Puzzles

3.1   Cuddly Bears

The hospital dressed all their teddy bears with bandages. Then they explained to the little children that the poor teddies had to stay at the hospital for their own health and recovery. The children reluctantly but sympathetically agreed.

3.2   The High-Society Dinner

The man who refused to be searched was an aristocrat who had fallen on very hard times but was trying to keep up appearances. He was so poor, however, that he could scarcely afford to eat. So, while at the dinner, he secretly lined his pockets with food from the table to keep him going for the next few days. Obviously if he was searched his secret would be revealed and he would be humiliated.

3.3   Eight Years Old

She was born on February 29, 1896. The year 1900 was not a leap year (only centuries divisible by 400 are leap years), so the next February 29 fell in 1904 when she was eight. She was twelve on her second birthday.

3.4 Cover That Hole

A square or rectangular manhole cover can fall down the hole, while a round manhole cover cannot. The square cover will fit down the diagonal of the hole (unless the rim it sits on is very large) but no matter how you turn a circle it never measures less than its diameter. So for safety and practicality all manhole covers should be round.

3.5 The Protagoras Paradox

This is a paradox with no clear-cut answer. Both parties have a good case. It would be interesting to see it argued out in court. Whoever lost could claim to have won—the student in losing would still not have won a case, Protagoras in losing would ensure a first victory for his pupil.

Some believe that the most likely outcome of such a situation, if it had come to trial, would have been victory for the student. He was after all under no obligation to practise law and up until that point he had not breached the contract. Once Protagoras had lost the first case, however, he could sue a second time on the grounds that the student had now won a case and was in breach of contract. Protagoras would therefore win the second case and recover his fees. Overall, Protagoras would have won.

The student would be smart to choose not to represent himself but to select a good lawyer who could win the first case for him. In that case, since the pupil would still not have won a case, he would have won the contest.

3.6 Hand in Glove

The manufacturer sent 5,000 right-hand gloves to Miami and 5,000 left-hand gloves to New York. He refused to pay the duty on them so both sets of gloves were impounded. Since nobody claimed them, both lots were subsequently sold off at auction. They went for a very low price (who wants 5,000 left-hand gloves?). Naturally, it was the clever Frenchman who won with a very low bid at each auction.

3.7 The School Superintendent

The teacher instructed her pupils always to raise their hands when a question was asked whether they knew the answer or not. If they did not know the answer they should raise their left hand. If they were sure they knew the answer they should raise their right hand. The teacher chose a different child each time, but always one who had raised his or her right hand.

3.8 No Trumps

It is equally likely that one couple will have all the trumps as that they will have no trumps between them. For if they have all the trumps it must mean that the other pair has none and vice versa.

3.9 How to Beat Nick Faldo

The challenger was a blind golfer and he arranged to play the champion at midnight on a dark night. The blind man was at no disadvantage in the dark but the champion could not see his ball to hit it. (Blind golfers do play matches and tournaments; they rely on others to indicate where their ball and the hole are.)

3.10 How to Beat Carl Lewis

He challenged the Olympic champion to run up a ladder. Since he was the fastest window cleaner in Ireland he won easily!

3.11 The Missing Furniture

The man was a circus lion tamer who had unfortunately forgotten his chair when he had to face a bad-tempered lion!

3.12 The Dead Man

The cord around the man's neck was a piece of rawhide

which he had soaked in water before entering the room. Once he had tied it tightly around his neck it naturally grew tighter and tighter as it dried.

3.13   The Busy Hospital

The wearing of seat belts was successful in reducing the number of deaths from road accidents. People who without seat belts would have been killed (and taken to the morgue) now survived but with injuries. Consequently more people were treated for injuries than before.

3.14   The Fallen Sign

The man knew the name of the town he had left that morning. So he replaced the sign so that it correctly named the direction he had come from. It would then be correct for all the other directions.

3.15   False Fingerprints

The man put his wife's big-toe print on the knife and left it beside the body. He could have used his own toe-print but that could have been later traced to him. Once his wife was buried, the "fingerprints" could never be traced.

3.16   Found, Lost, Found

The man fell overboard from a small boat at the seashore. He could not swim well and got into difficulties so he threw away the expensive and heavy binoculars around his neck. He was rescued. He then offered a swimmer a reward to dive down and recover his binoculars. This effort was unsuccessful. Later, however, when the tide went out he was able to pick them up off the sand.

3.17   The Crippled Child

This is a true story from India. The child was born into a family of beggars in Calcutta. The parents knew that a crippled child would earn more as a beggar than a healthy child would.

3.18   Insurance

This is a true story from Japan. The man was a keen golfer and his lifelong ambition was to score a hole in one. But this would prove very expensive as the custom at his golf club was that anyone who scored a hole in one had to buy all the other members a drink.

3.19   Eggs

A spherical or oval egg would roll in a straight line. However, an asymmetrical egg, which is narrower at one end than the other, will tend to roll in a circle. (Try it with a normal hen's egg.) If the eggs are on a cliff edge or other precarious place, the tendency to roll *around* rather than straight is a distinct advantage.

3.20   The Guard Dog

The boy brought along with him a female dog in heat. He released this dog into the orchard and the guard dog was thereby distracted.

3.21   The Last Message

The cassette had started at the beginning of the man's utterance. Who could have rewound it?

3.22   The Japanese Speaker

The businessman had been taught by a woman and he spoke Japanese like a woman. The speech intonation of men and women is very different in Japan, the masculine approach being more direct and aggressive. To hear a man speaking in a woman's style was unusual and amusing for the Japanese men.

4 Fiendish Puzzles

4.1 The Cellar Door

When the girl opened the cellar door she saw the living room and, through its windows, the garden. She had never seen these before because her parents had kept her all her life in the cellar. (This is a true lateral-thinking puzzler as nearly everyone makes the assumption that anyone opening the cellar door does so from outside the cellar.)

4.2 The Deadly Shot

The man died through suffocation. He was covered by an avalanche of snow which had been started by the sound of his gunshot as he stood at the foot of a snow-covered mountain.

4.3 Flat Out

Who said that the car was on the road? The car was being transported on the train.

4.4 An Odd Story

The first man put one lump of sugar in his coffee. That is an odd number. The second man put one lump in his coffee. That is also an odd number. The third man put 10 lumps in his coffee. That is a very odd number of lumps to put into a cup of coffee!

4.5 Free Maps

The aerial photography enabled a much clearer definition of land boundaries, and sizes. A tax on land at that time was based on its estimated area; and these had been largely underestimates. The new maps revealed correct land sizes and the government received more income from the land tax.

4.6   What a Shock I

The man was a prisoner who had been condemned to a very long jail sentence. He paid the prison undertaker to help him escape. The plan was that when the next prisoner died, the man would get into the coffin with the corpse. Later, after the coffin was buried outside the prison walls, the undertaker would dig it up to release the man.

When he heard that a man had died, the prisoner put his plan into action. In the dead of night he climbed into the coffin with the corpse. He fell asleep. He awoke after the burial and lit a match. He then saw that the face of the corpse was that of the undertaker!

4.7   What a Shock II

The man discovered a box containing four glass eyes mounted to a board with a dedication to their previous owners. They had belonged to the four previous husbands of his wife. The men had all died after about a year of marriage. This was the first that he had heard of them. He was recently married and had a glass eye!

4.8   The Deadly Party

The poison in the punch came from the ice cubes in it. When the man drank from the punch the ice had just been added and was still solid. Gradually, during the course of the evening, the ice melted contaminating the punch with the poison.

4.9   Speechless

The two men were both divers. They met one afternoon while scuba diving on the sea bed.

4.10   How to Hug

What the boy had picked up at the library was a volume of an encyclopedia. It was the section covering words beginning with H from How to Hug and that was what was printed on its cover.

4.11   The Healthy Dairymaids

Dairymaids caught the disease cowpox (a relatively harmless disease) from cows. This, however, gave them immunity from the related but much more dangerous disease smallpox. Jenner researched and developed the technique for inoculation with cowpox vaccine which eventually became widespread and overcame the bane of smallpox.

4.12   Toothache

When the man had been very poor he had entered into a contract with a Swedish medical institute. For a certain sum of money he promised them his body after his death for medical research. He later inherited money and asked to buy back this obligation. The institute refused, so he sued them in court. Not only did he lose his case, but the judge ordered him to pay the institute compensation for having had his teeth removed without the permission of their future owners!

4.13   The Lake Problem

You pour into the lake a known quantity of a concentrated chemical or vegetable dye. After allowing some time for the harmless chemical to disperse, you take samples of the water in several places. The more diluted the solution the greater the volume of water in the lake. Precise analysis of the concentration of chemicals in the samples would give a good estimate of the water volume of the lake.

4.14   The Realization

The man had just visited his wife in a hospital. She was on a life-support machine following a car accident. As he was walking down the stairs all the lights went out. There had been a power cut and the emergency back-up systems had failed. He knew immediately that his wife had died.

4.15   The Deadly Dish

The dish that the two men ordered was albatross, to remind themselves of when they had been stranded on a desert island many years earlier. When one of the men tasted it, he realized that he had never tasted albatross before. This meant that the meat he had been given to eat on the island was not albatross, as he had been told, but the flesh of his son who had died when they first reached the island.

4.16 Men in Uniform

The angry man was a convicted prisoner. He was being transported in the van and was handcuffed to a prison officer. When a suitable opportunity arose, the prisoner had produced a gun and demanded that the officer release him. The officer had put the key to the handcuffs in his mouth before struggling with the prisoner. The gun went off killing the officer but not before he had swallowed the key. The prisoner was therefore handcuffed to the body of the man he had just killed.

4.17 Healthy People I

The people were examined using a new technique called X-rays. Up until this time medical understanding of the human body was based largely on the dissection of corpses. This was always done on bodies lying horizontally. X-ray examinations were performed on people who were standing up. The difference caused many internal organs to have a different shape or position. Doctors misread this different appearance under X-ray to diagnose and treat problems which did not exist. They did not think laterally!

4.18 Healthy People II

The hospital was a maternity hospital and all those admitted were pregnant women.

4.19 The Grand Prix

Although the driver could not himself see around the curve, he could see the crowd in the stands ahead looking intently round the bend. He reasoned that they were not looking at him, a world-famous racing driver, because something more interesting, possibly a crash, had occurred around the curve.

4.20 The Stranger in the Car

The woman had died in childbirth. The stranger was the man's newborn son.

4.21 Eggshell Finish

The man was a professional clown. Each clown tries to have a unique face and copyrights his clown face by painting it on an eggshell which is then deposited with the international clown's club.

About the Authors

Paul Sloane was born in Scotland and grew up near Blackpool in the north of England. He studied Engineering at Trinity Hall, Cambridge, and graduated with a first-class honors degree. While at Cambridge he met his wife, who is a teacher. They live in Camberley, England, with their three daughters.

Most of Paul Sloane's career has been in the computer industry and he is currently the European vice-president for a software company. He has always been an avid collector and creator of puzzles. His first book, *Lateral Thinking Puzzlers*, was published by Sterling in 1991. Paul Sloane has given speeches and radio talks on the topic of change management and lateral thinking.

Des MacHale was born in County Mayo, Ireland, and is Associate Professor of Mathematics at University College in Cork. He was educated at University College, Galway, and the University of Keele in England. He and his wife, Anne, have five children.

The author of over thirty books, mostly of humor but also one on giving up smoking, Des MacHale has many interests including puzzles, geology, writing, broadcasting, films, photography, numismatics, and, of course, mathematics. He is currently working on three more books.

Sharing a strong interest in jokes and puzzles, and following a chance meeting in 1991, **Paul Sloane** and **Des MacHale** decided to cooperate on a book of problems. This work is the result.

PUZZLE INDEX

> Page key: **puzzle**, *clue*, solution

GREAT LATERAL THINKING PUZZLES

by Paul Sloane and Des MacHale

Acknowledgments

We would like to thank GAMES magazine for allowing us to reproduce puzzles which first appeared in their "How Come" Competition in 1992. These puzzles are: The Elder Twin by Judy Dean, The Seven-Year Itch by Dee Bruder, The Book by Dan Crawford, The Plane Crash by Lori Lavalle, Mountains Ahead by Bob Loper, High Office by Dave O'Brien, and A Good Night's Sleep by Kristen Stowe. Pat Squires contributed the idea in Suitcase for Hire.

CONTENTS

INTRODUCTION

Exercise is good for the brain. These puzzles form a sort of mental fitness course to stretch and develop your powers of lateral thinking. You may even get additional exercise when you hear the answers—if you kick yourself!

The puzzles consist of strange-sounding situations, often drawn from real life. Each has a perfectly good explanation. You have to figure out what it is. The Clues section provides hints when you are stumped. You will probably enjoy these puzzles more if you discuss them in a group rather than as a solitary reader. It is best if one person, knowing the solution, answers questions posed by the others in the group. Questions should be formed so that they can be answered either "yes," "no," or "irrelevant."

As you approach the puzzles, it is best to test all your assumptions. Ask broad questions to establish what is really happening in the situation. You will need to be logical and imaginative at the same time. When one line of questioning leads nowhere, you need to approach the problem from a fresh direction—that is what lateral thinking is all about.

The puzzles are arranged into four main groups with two WALLY Tests interspersed for light relief. The easier problems are in the Tempting Puzzles section and the most difficult ones come under Diabolical Puzzles. There is a section of Grisly Puzzles, all of which feature death, accident, or mutilation; these puzzles are among the most popular but they are not for the squeamish. The WALLY Tests are just for fun: they consist of trick questions deliberately designed to catch you out.

The world needs lateral thinkers, people who can bring a fresh approach to current problems in all walks of life. We need people who can develop imaginative new solutions. These puzzles are amusing diversions, but they may also help create a new legion of lateral thinkers.

THE PUZZLES

1 Tempting Puzzles

1.1 A Fishy Tale

A woman had a pet goldfish which she loved very dearly. One day she noticed that it was swimming feebly in its bowl and it looked very unwell. She rushed to the vet with her prized pet and he told her to come back in an hour. When she returned she found the goldfish swimming strongly and looking healthy again. How had the vet managed this?

1.2 The Lost Passenger

Little Billy was four years old and both his parents were dead. His guardian put him on a train to send him to a new home in the country. Billy could neither read nor write nor remember the address, so a large label on a string was secured around his neck clearly indicating Billy's name and destination. However, despite the best efforts and kindness of the railway staff, Billy never arrived at his new home. Why?

1.3 The Book

A woman walked up to a man behind a counter and handed him a book. He looked at it and said, "That will be four dollars." She paid the man and then walked out without the book. He saw her leave without it but did not call her back. How come?

1.4 A Hairy Problem

Why is it that, in general, the hair on a man's head goes grey before the hair in his moustache does?

1.5 The Birds

Two naturalists were walking in the country. They were both keen to protect the environment and to conserve nature and wildlife. One said to the other, "I was impressed by the way that you hit that bird." The second replied, "Yes, it was good, but not as good as that large bird that you hit earlier." What were they talking about?

1.6 Blinded at Teatime

A man was drinking a cup of tea when he was suddenly blinded. How?

1.7 Countdown

A man was slowly counting but unfortunately he miscounted. A little later he suffered a sharp pain in his back. Why?

1.8 Weather Forecast

John was watching television. Just after the midnight news there was a weather forecast: "It is raining now and will rain for the next two days. However, in 72 hours it will be bright and sunny." "Wrong again," snorted John. He was correct but how did he know?

1.9 No West

Let us agree that at the North Pole it is impossible to look north and at the South Pole it is impossible to look south. Then, where in the world would you be if you could look north and south but could not look east or west?

1.10 The Blind Beggar

A blind beggar had a brother who died. What relation was the blind beggar to the brother who died? ("Brother" is not the answer.)

1.11 The Truck Driver

A police officer saw a truck driver clearly going the wrong way down a one-way street, but did not try to stop him. Why not?

1.12 Mountains Ahead

You are seated next to the pilot of a small plane at an altitude of one mile. Huge mountains loom directly ahead. The pilot does not change speed, direction, or elevation, yet you survive. How come?

1.13 A Strange Christening

During a christening ceremony, the godmother of the child suddenly tackled the priest who was conducting the ceremony, knocked him down, and rolled him over on the ground. Why did she do this?

1.14 Pond Problem

A man wishes to reach the island in the middle of an ornamental lake without getting wet. The island is 20 feet from each edge of the pond (see diagram) and he has two planks each 17 feet long. How does he get across?

1.15 Walking and Running

There were two keen sportsmen. One evening at 6 P.M. one started walking at 4 miles per hour and the other started cycling at 12 miles per hour. After an hour each of them stopped. They then each ran for fifteen minutes at 8 miles per hour. They both started from the same place, A. They both kept heading in the same direction throughout and never changed course or rested during the entire 45 minutes. They both arrived at point B at the same time. How could this be and how far was it from A to B?

1.16 Church Bells I

A detective was lying in bed one Sunday morning listening to the local church bells ringing. Suddenly he realized that he was listening to a recording. How did he know?

1.17 Church Bells II

One night the vicar noticed that the old clock in the church tower struck 13 times at midnight. It did the same thing the following night so he had the mechanism investigated. It was found to be in perfect order, yet the clock struck 13 again that night. Why?

1.18 A Popular Book

When this book first came out it was read only by a handful of very rich people. Now almost everyone has a copy and reads it frequently. But you cannot buy it in a bookstore or borrow it from a library. What is it?

1.19 River Problem I

A man came to a river carrying a fox, a duck, and a bag of corn. There was a boat in which he could ferry one of the three items across the river at any one time. He could not leave the fox alone with the duck, nor the duck alone with the corn, so how did he get all three across?

1.20 River Problem II

This time the man reached the river with a fox, a duck, and a bag of corn, but this fox ate corn as well as ducks! There was the same boat as before in which he could take only one of the three with him. He could not leave the fox with either the corn or the duck, and, of course, the duck would gladly eat the corn if they were left together. How did he get all three across?

1.21 River Problem III

A man wishes to cross a wide, deep river, as shown in the diagram. There is no bridge, no boat, and he cannot swim. How does he get across?

1.22 Bill and Ben

Bill and Ben are identical twins. They are physically very alike, fit and healthy. They are both good runners and always run at the same speed. Each runs against the clock on the same track under the same conditions. Yet Ben takes ten times longer to finish than Bill. Why?

1.23 The Missing Brick

Note: This puzzle and the one that follows it are products of the same cruel and devious mind.

A young couple were inspecting a house they were considering buying. In the middle of the kitchen floor they found a single brick. The real estate agent did not know why it was there, nor did the builder, so they sent for the architect. He took the brick outside and threw it up into the air, whereupon the brick vanished from sight. What was happening?

1.24 A Strange Flight

A small plane was flying from Albany to New York some years ago. Seated beside each other were a grumpy old man smoking a foul pipe and a grumpy old lady with a noisy pet duck on her lap. Each spent most of the journey complaining about the other. Finally a compromise was reached. The old man agreed to throw his pipe out of the window if the old lady would throw her duck out. This was done. Just as the plane was about to land, the lady was pleased to see the duck flying alongside the plane. What did the duck have in its mouth?

WALLY Test I

Back by popular demand, here is the latest World Association for Laughter, Learning, and Youth (WALLY) test. It consists of questions designed to catch you out. Be warned! Every low, nasty trick we can devise has been used. Get a pencil and paper. Write down the answer to each question as soon as possible after reading it. You have two minutes to complete the test, starting now:

1. What is twice the half of $1\frac{3}{7}$?

2. If two peacocks lay two eggs in two days, how many eggs can one peacock lay in four days?

3. How many cubic feet of earth are there in a hole measuring 3 feet wide by 4 feet long by 5 feet deep?

4. Do you know how long cows should be milked?

5. Where was Queen Cleopatra's temple?

6. In what month do Americans eat the least?

7. How many marbles can you put in an empty bag?

8. The greengrocer stands 6 feet tall, has a 46-inch chest, and wears size 12 shoes. What do you think he weighs?

9. If a duck came paddling down the Nile, where would it have come from?

10. How long will a seven-day grandfather clock run without winding?

See WALLY Test solution on page 20.

2 Intriguing Puzzles

2.1 Stamp Collection

A keen stamp collector who specialized in U.S. stamps saw an advertisement offering a complete set of early U.S. stamps for a fraction of what it was worth. He quickly bought it. Although it was a genuine, splendid collection and a real bargain, he was angry, not pleased. What was going on?

2.2 Sheepish Behavior

On a cold winter's day, drivers found that sheep from the fields nearby kept coming onto the road. There was no snow and the road was not warmer than the fields but whenever the sheep were ushered back to the fields they quickly returned to the road. Why?

2.3 The Tennis Match

Pete challenged Jim to a tennis match for a large bet. Jim won the first set easily (6–1). Pete then offered to raise the stakes to ten times the amount. Jim readily agreed but lost the next two sets to Pete 6–1, 6–1. Pete tried hard throughout the match and never threw away a point. How did he manage to suddenly beat Jim easily?

2.4 Surrounded

A man was on the run from the police. He was relaxing, watching a play in a crowded theatre. Suddenly he noticed that detectives were closing in on him from all directions and were covering all exits. How did he escape?

2.5 The Banker

Bernard was the president of a major Wall Street bank. One morning when he got on a crowded train he was extremely worried. When the train stopped and he alighted, he felt very sick but he was not worried anymore. Why not?

2.6 A Curious Place

If you liked this place you would rather stay for a day than a year, but if you hated it you would rather stay for a year than a day. Why?

2.7 Grandmother's Letter

A boy at boarding school ran short of money so he wrote to his grandmother asking for a small contribution. The response was a letter containing a lecture on the evils of extravagance but no money of any kind. Nevertheless, the boy was very pleased. Why?

2.8 Theft at the Wedding

During a wedding reception the father of the bride found that his wallet was missing. How did he find out who had taken it?

2.9 The Free Extension

A man went to a builder with plans for an extension to his house. They had never met before but the builder agreed to build the extension at no charge to the man. Why?

2.10 Bridge Crossing

In wartime, an army had to cross a wide river. There were no boats and only one bridge, which was very narrow. Crossing the bridge would have made them sitting ducks for enemy gunfire. How did the entire army cross the river in relative safety?

2.11 The Seven-Year Itch

While digging a garden, a woman unearthed a large metal box filled with money and jewelry. For seven years she spent none of the money and told no one what she had found. Then she suddenly bought a new house, a new car, and a fur coat. How come?

2.12 Hit Out

A patient on the operating table is coming round after an operation. Suddenly he jumps up and strikes the surgeon as hard as he can. Why does he do this?

2.13 A Green Wedding

A clergyman was exasperated at having to sweep up vast amounts of confetti from the front of his church after every wedding. He decreed that in the future, if people insisted on throwing something at the married couple they throw something else. What did he suggest?

2.14 Sell the Truth

A manufacturer states that if middle-aged people told the truth more often he would sell a great deal more of his products. What does he manufacture?

2.15 The Dried Peas

In a sports shop there is a soccer ball containing a quantity of dried peas. Why are they there?

2.16 The Dog That Did Not Die

A mother told her six-year-old daughter that her pet dog had been hit by a car and killed. The little girl burst into tears. Half an hour later, the mother said that the dog was quite well and that it was all a mistake. Why did she do this?

2.17 High Office
. . . .

Tom cannot read or write or tie his shoes. He has never worked a day in his life. Despite these shortcomings, Tom is given an extremely important, prestigious, and well-paid job. How come?

2.18 The Follower
. . . .

A woman who was driving on her own pulled into a filling station and bought some gasoline. As she drove off she noticed a stranger in a car following her. She tried to shake him off by turning, accelerating, slowing down, etc. Finally she turned into a police station, but she was shocked to see him follow her in. He was not a policeman and there were no mechanical faults with her car. Why did he follow her?

2.19 Money to Burn
. . . .

A bank messenger, carrying a bag containing one thousand $100 bills, was robbed at gunpoint by a masked man. The man took the bag home and, without looking inside, he burnt it. Why?

2.20 Not a Kidnapper
. . . .

A banker was kidnapped and held tied up and blindfolded by a single kidnapper for several days. During this time he remained seated in a silent room and he never saw or heard his kidnapper. A ransom was paid and he was released. The police arrested a suspect who had a previous criminal record and had no alibi for the period of the crime. However, during questioning, the police inspector asked the suspect one thing and then released him. Why?

2.21. Ruination

In a factory in Buckinghamshire, England, in the nineteenth century, a bungling employee ruined an entire batch of the factory output. However, his employer was very pleased. Why?

2.22 The Bet

In the eighteenth century, long before the invention of the train or the motorcar, people delivered urgent messages using riders on horses. An English duke, a notorious gambler, once bet that he could have a letter delivered from one place to another 40 kilometers (about 25 miles) away in 45 minutes or less. This was much faster than a horse could travel. How did he win the bet?

WALLY Test I Answers

Here are the answers—get ready to kick yourself!

10. Without winding it will run for no time at all.
9. An egg.
8. Apples, pears, potatoes, etc.
7. One; after that it is not empty.
6. February; it has fewer days.
5. On the side of her forehead.
4. The same way that short cows are milked.
3. There is no earth in a hole.
2. Peacocks do not lay eggs.
1. 1¾.

Rate your score on the following scale:

Number Correct	Rating
8 to 10	Wally Whiz
6 to 7	Smart Alec
3 to 5	Wally
2 or less	Ultra Wally

2.23 Days Off

A man hired seven employees to work for him. After a few weeks he noticed that only six were ever at work on any day and that on each day a different one failed to show up for work. Why?

2.24 An Irish Puzzle

Chuck was an American on holiday in Ireland. His rental car broke down while he was in a little village and he was able to pull into a garage. There he asked how he could find someone to drive him back to Dublin. The man at the garage said, "I haven't been here long but I am sure that Milligan is your man. He lives in the big white house at the end of the village."

Chuck went up to the house and Milligan answered the door. "Can you drive me to Dublin?" asked Chuck. "No," answered Milligan and explained that in his old car he never drove outside the vicinity. However, as it was late he offered Chuck a room for the night. When Chuck awoke the next morning, he was shocked to see a huge golden eagle on the top of his wardrobe gazing down at him. Why did the man at the garage direct Chuck to Milligan?

3 Grisly Puzzles

3.1 A Shocking Discovery

A man met a beautiful woman in a bar. After a few drinks they agreed to go back to her apartment. In the morning he awoke in an alleyway having been drugged. He checked his wallet, watch and credit cards and found that none were missing. A few minutes later he discovered something which gave him a terrible shock. What was it?

3.2 Clean Sweep

A strong woman is about to start her cleaning job when she collapses in a faint. Why?

3.3 Death on the Boat

An expert sailor was killed while sailing his boat. He had suffered a heavy blow to the head. How had it happened?

3.4 A Rum Find

Two workmen were doing a major renovation job on an old English house. They could not believe their luck when they came upon a cask of excellent Jamaican rum. They indulged in a glass or two of this rum every day until finally it ran out. They then got a nasty surprise. What was it?

3.5 Broken Match

A man is found dead in a field. He is clutching a broken match. What happened?

3.6 The Cut Finger

A man is peeling potatoes when he cuts his finger. He immediately puts his hand into water and leaves it there for 30 seconds. However, when he pulls his hand out the cut has entirely disappeared. How can this have happened?

3.7 The Music Stopped

The music stopped. She died. Explain.

3.8 The Dog Choker

A woman came home to find her dog choking in the hall. She rushed the dog to a nearby vet and went home while he examined the dog. When she arrived home the phone was ringing. It was the vet warning her to get out of the house at once. Why?

3.9 The Movie

Tom and Joe went to a movie. There were many other people there. During a quiet scene, Tom drew a gun. Joe screamed, "Don't shoot!" but Tom shot him. Tom then left. Many people saw Tom leave and they restrained him. The police arrived and quickly released Tom. Why?

3.10 Damaged Car

A man was the proud owner of a beautiful and expensive

Mercedes sports car. One day he drove it to an isolated parking area and then smashed the window, scratched the doors, and ripped out the radio. Why?

3.11 The Motorcyclist

A man is lying severely injured in the road. He had quite deliberately stepped out from the sidewalk in front of a motorcyclist who had hit him. Why had the man done this?

3.12 Swimmer in the Forest

Deep in the forest, a forest ranger found the body of man dressed only in swimming trunks, snorkel, and facemask. The nearest lake was 8 miles away and the sea was 100 miles away. How did he die?

3.13 The Dark Room

A man walked into a small, dark room in a large building. After a few minutes he emerged from the dark room and left the building. A man then walked up to him and shot him dead. Why?

3.14 The Two Vans

In a bizarre accident, two identical vans simultaneously plunged over a dockside and into thirty feet of water. They both landed upright. Each van had a driver who was fit, uninjured by the fall, and conscious. One drowned but the other easily escaped. Why?

3.15 Suicide

A man wakes up in a dark room. He switches on the light. A few minutes later he shoots himself. Why?

3.16 The Plane Crash

Susan watched as her husband boarded the 8:15 P.M. Air Canada flight from Toronto to Chicago. She then drove home from the airport and proceeded to watch a movie. About one hour into the movie there was a news flash; the 8:15 P.M. Air Canada flight from Toronto to Chicago had crashed with no survivors. Susan did not react. She just continued to watch the movie. How come?

3.17 One Beautiful Morning

A man woke up on a beautiful summer morning. He went to the window, looked out in horror, and then shot himself. Why?

3.18 The Blanket Mystery

A man walked up a hill carrying a blanket. Because of this, one hundred people died. How?

3.19 The Deadly Bite

A woman gave a man something to eat. It caused him to die. It was not poisoned or poisonous. Why did he die?

3.20 Bad Boy

A man sitting at home was killed by a little boy who was outside. How?

26

. . . .

WALLY Test II

. . . .

Just when you thought you were safe—another WALLY test! As before, get a pencil and paper. Write down the answer to each question as soon as possible after reading it. You have two minutes to complete the test, starting now:

1. If a ton of coal costs $30 and a ton of coke costs $25, what will a ton of firewood come to?

2. Removing an appendix is called an appendectomy, removing tonsils is called a tonsillectomy. What is it called when they remove a growth from your head?

3. Why are U.S. soldiers forbidden to carry rifles any longer?

4. What three things that you can eat can you never have for breakfast?

5. If a farmer raises wheat in dry weather, what does he raise in wet weather?

6. What would you call a person who did not have all his fingers on one hand?

7. Which is greater, six dozen dozen or half a dozen dozen?

8. What is the best way to get down from a camel?

9. How could a man be severely injured by being hit by some tomatoes?

10. Why do Chinese men eat more rice than Japanese men?

See WALLY Test solution on page 35.

4 Diabolical Puzzles

4.1 The Nursery Rhyme

A man is visiting a young couple who have a one-year-old daughter. He takes the baby on his knee and, with the parents present, begins to recite a nursery rhyme with the child. Within a few moments, however, he is cringing with embarrassment. Why?

4.2 The Elder Twin

One day, Kerry celebrated her birthday. Two days later, her older twin brother, Terry, celebrated his birthday. How come?

4.3 Fair Shares

To divide a cake equally between two people you let one cut and the other choose. How could you divide a cake among three or more people fairly? No protractors, rulers, or measuring devices are involved, just a knife.

4.4 The Sealed Envelope

One morning a jealous wife found in the mail a letter addressed to her husband. How did she remove the letter from the sealed envelope without breaking the seal or tearing the envelope and then put it back in the envelope so that her husband did not know that the letter had been read?

4.5 Tattoo

Why did a significant number of people have a Crucifixion scene tattooed on their bodies? These people did not share any particular religious beliefs.

4.6 Suitcase for Hire

Pat went into a luggage shop to buy a suitcase. The assistant said, "It is most unusual to buy a suitcase. Why don't you rent one like all our other customers?" Why should this be so?

4.7 The Tennis Tournament

A total of 213 people enter a knockout tennis tournament. What is the least number of matches that must be played to decide an overall winner?

4.8 The Key

Every night before he went to bed, a man carefully locked all the doors of his house. Then he placed the front-door key inside a bucket of cold water. In the morning he retrieved the key from the bucket in order to open the door. Why did he do this?

4.9 That's Fast!

While Harry was working in his garage he made something travel at over 3000 miles (4800 kilometers) per hour. What on earth was it?

4.10 A Man in a Bar

A man walked into a bar and asked for a certain drink. The bartender apologized that he had run out of that particular drink but he offered the man any other drink in the house free. The man refused and walked out. Why?

4.11 The 88 Hours

A man sat perfectly still for 88 hours. Why?

4.12 Sand Trap

Why did a man go to great trouble to bury in the desert fifteen brand-new Mercedes-Benz cars, all greased and wrapped in plastic?

4.13 Building Demolition

In Australia a perfectly good building was demolished and an almost identical one erected on exactly the same site. The original building was in good condition, it had no defects and there was no issue of safety or planning permission. Why was it demolished?

4.14 The Torn Cheque

A man writes a cheque, signs it, and then tears it into exactly 217 pieces. He then puts it in the mail. Can you give a rational explanation for his behavior?

4.15 The Weather Report

A terse weather report once stated that the temperature in a certain place at midnight on June 1st was a certain number of degrees. Where was the place?

4.16 Odd Animals

What do these animals have in common: koala bear, prairie dog, firefly, silkworm, jackrabbit, guinea pig?

4.17 The Shorter Program

A music program on a well-respected radio station finished exactly eight minutes earlier than it was scheduled to. An embarrassed official gave the explanation for this mistake. What was it? How long was the program supposed to last? (It is possible to work this out.)

4.18 Traffic Trouble

How did a change in state traffic regulations lead to an increase in trade for local sex shops? (The answer is not obscene!)

4.19 Blackmail

A rather nasty criminal developed a seemingly foolproof way of extracting money from bereaved families. He would scan the obituary columns in order to choose the name of a wealthy man who had recently died. Then he sent an invoice for pornographic books addressed to the man and claiming payment for goods previously despatched. To avoid any scandal the family would invariably pay. How was he eventually caught out?

4.20 A Good Night's Sleep

A man in a hotel was unable to sleep. He got up, opened the window drapes, went back to bed and fell asleep easily. How come?

4.21 Grateful for Poor Service

A man saw something advertised at a certain price and went to buy it. An official refused to sell it to him even though the man could pay and other men and women were sold it. Later the man was very glad that his purchase had been refused. Why was he refused and why was he glad?

4.22 Free T-shirts

A man was watching television when he saw an advertisement offering free T-shirts to the first 100 viewers who phoned in. He called the number given, stated his size, and received his free T-shirt in a few days. Later he very much regretted doing this. Why?

4.23 Bank Robbery I

A gang robbed a bank. They tied up the staff and then hurriedly left the bank. One of the bank staff struggled free and did something which quickly led to the apprehension of the gang. What was it?

4.24 Bank Robbery II

A gang stole a bank security van containing over $700,000. Their plan was executed perfectly and they got clean away. The police had no trace of them and the gang were free to divide and spend the loot. However, they were extremely frustrated. Why?

4.25 A Puzzling Attack

Four rational and reasonable people were seated around a table. Suddenly three of them jumped up and viciously beat the fourth one senseless. Why?

WALLY Test II Answers

More answers—more groans!

10. There are more of them.

9. They were tinned tomatoes.

8. You cannot get down from a camel. You get down from a duck.

7. Six dozen dozen; it is 12 times as much as half a dozen dozen.

6. Normal; your fingers should be equally spread over two hands.

5. An umbrella.

4. Lunch, dinner, and supper.

3. The rifles are long enough already.

2. A haircut.

1. Ashes.

Rate your score on the following scale:

Number Correct	Rating
8 to 10	Wally Whiz
6 to 7	Smart Alec
3 to 5	Wally
2 or less	Ultra Wally

THE CLUES

1 Tempting Puzzles

1.1 A Fishy Tale

Q: Did the vet change the water?
A: No.

Q: Did he give the fish any medication, food, or tonic?
A: No.

Q: Had the woman had the goldfish for a long time?
A: Yes.

1.2 The Lost Passenger

Q: Did someone deliberately harm or abduct Billy?
A: No.

Q: Was his label removed in some way?
A: Yes.

Q: Was Billy a little boy?
A: No.

Q: Did Billy destroy the name tag?
A: Yes. (He ate it!)

1.3 The Book

Q: Was he surprised that she left without the book?
A: No.

Q: Did she pay the money to buy the book?
A: No.

Q: When she gave him the money, did she receive something in return?
A: No, not really, but she was quite happy to pay it.

1.4 A Hairy Problem

Q: Is this to do with the way the hair is cut, brushed, washed, or treated in any way?
A: No.

Q: Is it to do with eating, drinking, thinking, or talking?
A: No.

Q: Is it to do with timing?
A: Yes.

1.5 The Birds

Q: Had they each physically hit something?
A: Yes.

Q: Had they hit living or dead creatures?
A: No, neither.

Q: Had one of them hit an eagle?

A: Yes.

1.6 Blinded at Teatime

Q: Was there a flash of light or some other external occurrence?
A: No.

Q: Was the man physically normal?
A: Yes.

Q: Did something go into his eye?
A: Yes.

Q: Did this go into his eye because he was drinking the cup of tea?
A: Yes.

1.7 Countdown

Q: Was he counting as part of a task he was performing?
A: Yes.

Q: Was anyone else involved?
A: No.

Q: Would this happen to a woman?
A: Probably not.

Q: Was the pain caused by a pointed metal object?
A: Yes.

1.8   Weather Forecast

Q: Was John some kind of weather expert?
A: No.

Q: Did he have some special knowledge or insight into the future?
A: No.

Q: Is this to do with timing?
A: Yes.

1.9   No West

Q: Is there a place where it would be impossible to look east or west?
A: Yes.

Q: Is this because east and west are meaningless terms at this place?
A: Yes.

Q: Has anyone ever been there?
A: No.

1.10   The Blind Beggar

Q: Were the blind beggar and the brother both humans?
A: Yes.

Q: Did the brother and the beggar have the same parents?
A: Yes.

Q: Were they brothers?
A: No.

1.11   The Truck Driver

Q: Did the police officer and the truck driver both know that it was against the law to drive the wrong way down a one-way street?
A: Yes.

Q: Was there some emergency which justified either of their actions?
A: No.

Q: Should the policeman have taken action?
A: No.

Q: Was the truck driver committing a violation?
A: No.

1.12   Mountains Ahead

Q: Does the pilot have control of the aircraft throughout?
A: Yes.

Q: Is there a tunnel or hole or other way through the mountains?
A: No.

Q: Were you at any time in serious danger?
A: No.

Q: Did you fly over, around, or past the mountains?
A: No.

1.13   A Strange Christening

Q: Was this a normal priest conducting a normal christening?
A: Yes.

Q: Was there a good reason for her actions?
A: Yes.

Q: Did she act to protect or help the baby?
A: No.

Q: Did she act to help or protect the priest?
A: Yes.

1.14 Pond Problem

This is so easy that no clue should be needed. However, it can be said that he used no other equipment and no counterbalancing weight. He merely arranged the planks.

1.15 Walking and Running

Q: Did the sportsmen travel in a circle?
A: No. They travelled in a straight line from A to B.

Q: Does this involve going backwards, sideways, up, or down?
A: No.

Q: Did they both travel exactly the same distance?
A: Yes.

Q: Was it a normal bicycle?
A: No.

1.16 Church Bells I

Q: Was it just the sound of the bells which indicated to him that it was a recording?
A: Yes.

Q: Was it to do with the number of times that the bells chimed?
A: No.

Q: Did he hear some additional sound which should not have been there?
A: No.

Q: Was the clue the absence of something which should have been heard?
A: Yes.

1.17 Church Bells II

Q: Did it strike 13 at midday?
A: No. It struck 12.

Q: Was this fault due to the clock mechanism?
A: No.

Q: Was a bird, bat, or insect involved?
A: No.

Q: Was the 13th strike caused by some human action?
A: Yes.

1.18 A Popular Book

Q: Do people read it frequently?
A: Yes.

Q: Do people read it from start to finish?
A: No.

Q: Does it contain a lot of useful information?
A: Yes.

1.19   River Problem I

This is an old chestnut which can be solved by leaving things, taking things, and coming back for things. If you play around with the possibilities you will soon arrive at the answer. When you do, do not relax just yet; the next puzzle will test your mettle.

1.20   River Problem II

This solution requires more lateral thinking than the last puzzle. He made it safely across with all three items. At no time was the fox left alone with the duck or the corn. Nor was the duck left alone with the corn. Yet the boat could contain only the man and one of his charges at any one time.

1.21   River Problem III

The man uses a piece of rope. But how?

1.22   Bill and Ben

Q: Does Bill run exactly as fast as Ben?
A: Yes.

Q: Do they both start in the same place and finish in the same place?
A: Yes.

Q: Does Ben run further than Bill?
A: Yes.

Q: Is the course somehow more difficult for Ben?
A: Yes.

Q: Is it a normal racetrack?
A: No.

1.23 The Missing Brick

Q: In solving this problem, does anything about the house, the brick, the couple, or the other people involved matter?
A: No.

Q: Does what went before this matter?
A: No.

Q: Does what follows this matter?
A: Yes.

1.24 A Strange Flight

Q: Did the duck have the pipe in its mouth?
A: No.

Q: Did the duck have something else in its mouth?
A: Yes.

Q: Does anything about the old man, the old lady, or the plane matter?
A: No.

Q: Does what happened before matter?
A: Yes.

2 Intriguing Puzzles

2.1 Stamp Collection

Q: Did he recognize the collection?
A: Yes.

Q: Was it a genuine stamp collection worth a lot of money?
A: Yes.

Q: Had he previously sold it or given it away?
A: No.

Q: Did he previously own all the stamps which were in this collection?
A: Yes.

Q: So he now had a set of duplicates?
A: No.

2.2 Sheepish Behavior

Q: Did the sheep come onto the road in order to be warmer or better protected than in the fields?
A: No.

Q: Did they come onto the road in order to get away from something in the fields?
A: No.

Q: Was there something which attracted them to the road?
A: Yes.

Q: Does this happen only in very cold weather?
A: Yes.

44

2.3 The Tennis Match

Q: Did they both use the same court, net, balls, and rackets for the three sets?

A: Yes. Nothing about the environment or equipment changed.

Q: Did Pete's game improve or Jim's deteriorate?

A: Pete's game improved. Jim's play stayed the same.

Q: To an outside observer, would Pete have appeared to have been trying his hardest during the first set?

A: Yes.

Q: Did Pete change something which caused his play to dramatically improve?

A: Yes.

2.4 Surrounded

Q: Had the detectives seen him and were they intent on arresting him?

A: Yes.

Q: Did he escape across the stage?

A: No.

Q: Did he use the audience to help him escape?

A: Yes.

2.5 The Banker

Q: Was Bernard worried about business?

A: No.

Q: Was he worried about his safety?

A: Yes.

Q: Was any kidnapping, robbery, or criminal activity involved or the cause of his worry?

A: No.

Q: Was he normally worried on trains?
A: No. He travelled to work on one every day.

Q: Was anyone with him?
A: Yes. His nephew.

Q: Was the nephew worried?
A: No. He was happy.

2.6 A Curious Place

Q: Is it a town or a building?
A: No.

Q: Is this a real or an imaginary place?
A: A real place.

Q: Is it a pleasant place to be?
A: No.

Q: Is it a dangerous place?
A: Yes (but irrelevant).

Q: Has anyone ever been there for a day?
A: No.

2.7 Grandmother's Letter

Q: Was the stamp or the envelope valuable?
A: No.

Q: Was there something of value in the envelope?
A: Yes.

Q: Was he pleased because he somehow got some money?
A: Yes.

2.8 Theft at the Wedding

Q: Did he somehow manage to get everybody to empty their pockets?
A: No.

Q: Was it anything to do with the contents of the wallet?
A: No.

Q: Did he discover the culprit immediately or sometime later?
A: Sometime later.

2.9 The Free Extension

Q: Did the builder gain some benefit from this whole process?
A: Yes. Definitely.

Q: Were the two men related or was there an existing business relationship between them?
A: No.

Q: Did the man subsequently provide some service, reward, or payment to the builder?
A: No.

Q: Was the man famous?
A: Yes.

2.10 Bridge Crossing

Q: Did they cross at night?
A: No.

Q: Did they use the bridge?
A: No.

Q: Did they swim across?
A: No.

Q: Did they get wet?
A: Yes.

2.11 The Seven-Year Itch

Q: Did the woman wait in order to avoid observation by the police or criminals?
A: No.

Q: Was the money and jewelry stolen?
A: Yes (but irrelevant).

Q: Would she have liked to have spent the money earlier?
A: Yes!

Q: Was she somehow physically prevented from spending the money?
A: Yes.

Q: Was she in prison?
A: No.

2.12   Hit Out

Q: Did the patient have some grievance against the surgeon?
A: No.

Q: Was the surgeon a genuine surgeon who had carried out a proper surgical operation on the patient?
A: Yes.

Q: Does the nature of the operation matter?
A: No.

Q: Does the profession of the patient matter?
A: Yes.

2.13   A Green Wedding

Q: Did the cleric suggest something which would not need to be cleared up?
A: Yes.

Q: Is it something which is non-polluting and disappears in a short time?
A: Yes.

Q: Does it involve water in some form?
A: No.

48

2.14 Sell the Truth

Q: Does he manufacture something used by people of all ages?
A: Yes.

Q: Is his product in common use?
A: Yes.

Q: Would he sell more if middle-aged people were more honest about their appearance, health, size, or weight?
A: No.

Q: Would he sell more if middle-aged people were more honest about their age?
A: Yes.

2.15 The Dried Peas

Q: Do customers buy the ball containing the dried peas for a specific purpose?
A: Yes.

Q: Do the purchasers play soccer with this ball?
A: Yes.

Q: Do they keep the peas inside the ball, or take them out?
A: The peas stay inside the ball.

Q: Do they play a special game with this ball?
A: No. They play regular soccer as well as they can.

2.16 The Dog That Did Not Die

Q: Was the girl's dog unharmed throughout?
A: Yes.

Q: Had the mother been misinformed?
A: No.

Q: Did the mother deliberately lie to her daughter?
A: Yes.

Q: Did she do this out of spite or malice, or to punish or threaten her daughter?
A: No.

Q: Did she do this for a particular reason and was she successful in her aim?
A: Yes.

2.17 High Office

Q: Was Tom chosen for a specific reason?
A: Yes.

Q: Does Tom have some particular skill or aptitude?
A: No.

Q: Could anyone be given this job?
A: No.

Q: Was the previous holder of the job able to read, write, etc.?
A: Yes, he was very accomplished.

2.18 The Follower

Q: Was he a danger to her?
A: No.

Q: Was he trying to help her?
A: Yes.

Q: Had he seen something wrong with her car?
A: No.

2.19 Money to Burn

Q: Does this involve some kind of insurance claim?
A: No.

Q: Did the robber know what was in the bag?
A: Yes.

Q: Was the messenger part of the plot?

A: No. He was honest.

Q: Was the money genuine?
A: No. It was counterfeit.

2.20 Not a Kidnapper

Q: Was the banker able to give any clue about the kidnapper?
A: No.

Q: Did the suspect have a physical or mental disability?
A: No.

Q: Did he have some trait or characteristic which indicated that he had not committed this crime?
A: Yes.

Q: Was it something you would immediately see or hear or recognize if you met him?
A: No.

Q: Was it something which you would recognize if you watched him over a period of time?
A: Yes.

2.21 Ruination

Q: Did the employee save the company from some disaster or major cost?
A: No.

Q: Was the employee rewarded or punished?
A: Rewarded.

Q: Was it an accident?
A: Yes.

Q: Was the ruined output somehow more valuable?
A: Yes.

Q: What sort of products did the factory produce?
A: Paper.

2.22 The Bet

Q: Did he actually have a letter transported that distance in 45 minutes?
A: Yes.

Q: Did he use cannons, guns, gunpowder, or explosives?
A: No.

Q: Was the starting point somewhere unusual, such as the top of a mountain or cliff?
A: No. His method would work in any open country.

Q: Did he use horses or some other running animal?
A: No.

Q: Did his method involve considerable preparation and help?
A: Yes.

2.23 Days Off

Q: Did the employees deliberately collaborate in order for each to have a day off?
A: No.

Q: Was there some connection or association between the employees other than their work?
A: No.

Q: Did each one always take the same day of the week off?
A: Yes.

Q: Does the type or place of work matter?
A: No.

Q: Were they similar in culture or nationality?
A: No. They were quite different.

2.24 An Irish Puzzle

Q: Did the man at the garage know Milligan personally or have any connection with him?
A: No.

Q: Did Milligan ever drive anybody anywhere?
A: No.

Q: Was the eagle a genuine eagle?
A: Yes.

Q: Was it alive?
A: No.

Q: Is Milligan's profession important?
A: Yes.

3 Grisly Puzzles

3.1 A Shocking Discovery

Q: Had he been deceived and robbed?
A: Yes.

Q: Was anything missing from his wallet or pockets, or his
jewelry or clothes?
A: No.

Q: Did he find something new which gave him the shock?
A: Yes.

Q: Was it on his body?
A: Yes.

3.2   Clean Sweep

Q: Was her cleaning job in a shop, office, school, or factory?
A: No.

Q: Was her fainting caused by something she saw?
A: Yes.

Q: Was it a body or part of a body?
A: Yes.

Q: Was it a surprise for her to see a body?
A: No.

3.3   Death on the Boat

Q: Was his death an accident?
A: Yes.

Q: Was anyone else on the boat at the time of his death?
A: No.

Q: Had he been hit by anything on or part of the boat?
A: No.

Q: Was any bird, fish, or marine mammal involved?
A: No.

Q: Had he been hit by something which fell out of the sky?
A: Yes.

3.4 A Rum Find

Q: Was the rum poisoned in some way?
A: No.

Q: Was it genuine rum?
A: Yes.

Q: Did the cask contain something other than the rum?
A: Yes.

3.5 Broken Match

Q: Was the match instrumental in the man's death?
A: Yes.

Q: Was he trying to light something with the match prior to his death?
A: No.

Q: Was he alone in the field?
A: Yes.

Q: Did he know he was going to die before he entered the field?
A: Yes.

Q: Was he murdered?
A: No.

Q: Did he fall into the field?
A: Yes.

3.6 The Cut Finger

Q: Was the cut healed?
A: No.

Q: Did he put his hand into a sink or a bowl?
A: No.

Q: Was he outdoors when this happened?
A: Yes.

Q: Was he pleased when he drew his hand out of the water?
A: No.

3.7 The Music Stopped

Q: Did she die because the music stopped?
A: Yes.

Q: Was the music some kind of signal?
A: Yes.

Q: Was she doing something dangerous?
A: Yes.

Q: Was it some kind of entertainment?
A: Yes.

3.8 The Dog Choker

Q: Was the dog a guard dog?
A: Yes.

Q: Had the vet found evidence of poison or gas?
A: No.

Q: Had the vet deduced that there was a danger in the house?
A: Yes.

Q: Had the vet discovered what it was the dog was choking on?
A: Yes.

3.9 The Movie

Q: Were they in a normal cinema?
A: Yes.

Q: Did any of the other people there notice the murder?
A: Yes. Everyone did.

Q: Did the police release Tom because he was innocent of any crime?
A: Yes.

Q: Did Tom shoot Joe in self-defense?
A: No.

Q: Were the people who restrained Tom angry with him?
A: No.

3.10 The Damaged Car

Q: Did he do this to claim on insurance?
A: No.

Q: Did he deliberately and voluntarily damage his own car?
A: Yes.

Q: Was there a monetary reason for doing this?
A: No.

Q: Did he set out that day intending to damage his car?
A: No.

Q: Did something happen which caused him to damage his car?
A: Yes.

Q: Did he do it because he wanted to avoid some worse consequence?
A: Yes.

3.11 The Motorcyclist

Q: Was the man trying to injure or kill himself?
A: No.

Q: Did he know the motorcyclist who hit him?
A: No.

Q: Did he expect the motorcyclist to stop?
A: Yes.

Q: Was the motorcyclist expecting the man to step out in front of him?
A: No.

Q: Did the man's profession have something to do with motorcycling?
A: Yes.

3.12 Swimmer in the Forest

Q: Did he die at the spot where he was found?
A: Yes.

Q: Had he previously been swimming?
A: Yes.

Q: Was he taken to the forest against his will?
A: Yes.

Q: Was he taken deliberately?
A: No, accidentally.

3.13 The Dark Room

Q: Would the man have been shot if he had not entered the dark room?
A: No.

Q: Did he do something in the dark room which directly led to his being shot?
A: Yes.

Q: Did this happen during a war?
A: It could have happened in peacetime or war but is more likely during a war.

Q: Were either of the men in uniform?
A: No.

3.14 The Two Vans

Q: Can we consider the vans, their situations, and the fitness and skills of the drivers to be identical at the time of this accident?
A: Yes.

Q: Was one able to open a door and escape and the other not?
A: Yes.

Q: Did one of them do something different (and smarter) than the other?
A: Yes.

Q: If they had been driving cars rather than vans would the outcome have been different?
A: Yes. They would probably both have drowned.

3.15 Suicide

Q: Did some noise or action wake him?
A: No. He awoke naturally.

Q: Did he commit suicide because something happened which caused him to realize something?
A: Yes.

Q: Did he see something which caused the realization?
A: No.

Q: Did he hear something which caused the realization?
A: Yes.

Q: Was there anyone else in the house?
A: No.

Q: Was it a special kind of house?
A: Yes.

3.16 The Plane Crash

Q: Was the news flash a genuine one or was it part of the movie?
A: It was a genuine news flash.

Q: Was the news flash accurate: had the plane crashed with no survivors?
A: Yes.

Q: Had the woman's husband got off the flight before it left?
A: No.

Q: Had she planned the plane crash or did she know it would happen?
A: No.

Q: Did she know that her husband had not been killed?
A: Yes.

3.17 One Beautiful Morning

Q: Did the man see something unusual, terrible, or frightening from the window?
A: No.

Q: Did he commit suicide because it was a beautiful morning?
A: Yes.

Q: Had he done something terrible which he now regretted?
A: Yes.

Q: Is his profession important?
A: Yes. He was a preacher.

3.18   The Blanket Mystery

Q: Did the man inadvertently cause an accident?
A: No.

Q: Did he somehow deliberately cause the deaths of the people?
A: He deliberately caused their deaths.

Q: Did he kill them or did he have accomplices who killed them?
A: His accomplices killed them.

Q: Were the people who died travelling when this happened?
A: Yes.

Q: Could this have happened recently?
A: No. It happened during the nineteenth century.

3.19   The Deadly Bite

Q: Did she know it was dangerous?
A: Yes.

Q: Did the man know it was dangerous?
A: Yes.

Q: Did the food contain some medical or physical danger?
A: No.

Q: Did he die soon afterwards?
A: No. He died many years afterwards.

Q: What kind of food was it?
A: Fruit.

3.20   Bad Boy

Q: Did the boy take some deliberate action which resulted
in the man's death?
A: Yes.

Q: Does this involve firearms, electricity, or water?
A: No.

Q: Did the boy mean to kill the man?
A: No.

Q: Did the boy enter the house or put something into the
house?
A: No.

4 Diabolical Puzzles

4.1 The Nursery Rhyme

Q: Did the baby do something on him?
A: No. The baby was as good as gold.

Q: Was the choice of nursery rhyme inappropriate?
A: Yes, very.

Q: Did he discover something about the baby in the course of reciting the rhyme?
A: Yes.

4.2 The Elder Twin

Q: Were Kerry and Terry genuine human twins, born of the same mother of the same pregnancy?
A: Yes.

Q: Was Terry, the older twin, born before Kerry?
A: Yes.

Q: Was her birthday always before his?
A: Yes.

Q: Does where the births took place matter?
A: Yes.

4.3 Fair Shares

Q: Does the solution involve weighing or measuring?
A: No.

Q: Does the solution involve cutting the cake and letting people choose?
A: Yes.

Q: Is the cake cut one piece at a time?
A: Yes.

Q: Is the system fair—that is, no one can complain that someone else has received too large a piece or that they themselves have received too small a piece?
A: Yes.

4.4 The Sealed Envelope

Q: Did the wife somehow open and then re-seal the envelope?
A: No.

Q: Did she replace the original envelope with another?
A: No.

Q: Can this be done with an ordinary envelope and letter?
A: Generally speaking, yes it can; but not always.

Q: Did she use some kind of tool?
A: Yes. A kind of needle.

4.5 Tattoo

Q: Were they trying to identify themselves in some way?
A: No.

Q: Did they share a common occupation?
A: Yes.

Q: Does where they were tattooed matter?
A: Yes, it was on their backs.

Q: Did this happen recently?
A: No, about two centuries ago.

4.6 Suitcase for Hire

Q: Was the shop a rental-only shop?
A: No.

Q: Did most customers at this shop choose to rent their suitcases rather than buy them?

A: Yes.

Q: Did this have anything to do with price, or insurance, or choice of style?
A: No.

Q: Did people rent because of convenience?
A: Yes.

Q: Was Pat in the United States?
A: No.

4.7 The Tennis Tournament

There is a simple, logical, and lateral way of working out the number of matches in such a knockout tournament whatever the number of entries. Try thinking in terms of winners and losers.

4.8 The Key

Q: Was this a regular man in a regular house with a regular key?
A: Yes.

Q: Did he put the key in the bucket of water to prevent some person or some creature getting it?
A: No.

Q: Does this involve criminal intent or the prevention of criminal action?
A: No.

Q: Did he do this to protect the safety of himself or his wife?
A: Yes.

Q: Was it to protect against a likely accident?
A: Yes.

4.9 That's Fast!

Q: Does this involve gases, atoms, or tiny particles?
A: No.

Q: Did Harry have special equipment or skills?
A: No. Anyone can do this.

Q: Did he intend to do this?
A: No.

Q: Did whatever travelled at that high speed make a very
   loud noise?
A: It made a noise, but not a very loud noise.

Q: Did it travel very far?
A: No, only about two feet.

4.10 A Man in a Bar

Q: Did the two men know each other?
A: No.

Q: Was the man thirsty?
A: No.

Q: Did he really want the drink?
A: Yes.

Q: Was it some kind of signal or message?
A: No.

Q: What kind of drink was it?
A: Wine.

4.11 The 88 Hours

Q: Did he sit still voluntarily?
A: No. He sat down voluntarily but thereafter he would
   have preferred to get up.

Q: Was he physically restrained in the chair?
A: Yes.

Q: Does this involve any criminal intent?
A: No.

Q: Was he rewarded for sitting still for so long?
A: No.

Q: Was he in good health when he sat down?
A: No. He had a bad toothache.

4.12 Sand Trap

Q: Were the cars stolen?
A: No. He had bought them legitimately.

Q: Did he bury them to make some financial gain?
A: Yes.

Q: Did he intend that they be dug up later when something had changed?
A: Yes.

Q: Was he taking advantage of unusual circumstances?
A: Yes.

4.13 Building Demolition

Q: Did the original building have some flaw or defect which made it necessary for it to be replaced?
A: No.

Q: Was the new building significantly better in some way?
A: No.

Q: Were both new and old buildings used for the same purpose?
A: Yes.

Q: Is that purpose relevant to the solution of this puzzle?
A: Yes.

Q: Did the building contain something of value?
A: Yes.

4.14 The Torn Cheque

Q: Is the number 217 relevant?
A: Yes.

Q: Is he sending the cheque to his ex-wife or to anyone he knows personally?
A: No.

Q: Is the cheque for the taxman or some other official?
A: No.

Q: Does the recipient of the cheque like puzzles?
A: No.

Q: Is he angry with the person to whom he is sending the cheque?
A: Yes.

4.15 The Weather Report

Q: Is it possible to deduce where this is from the information given?
A: Yes.

Q: Did the weather report give any other details?
A: No.

Q: Did the weather report state whether the temperature was in degrees Fahrenheit or Celsius?
A: No.

4.16 Odd Animals

These animals all have something quite specific in common. However, it has nothing to do with habitat, foodstuffs, appearance, activity, procreation, zoos, or physical attributes. What can it be?

4.17 The Shorter Program

Q: Was this a live concert which finished early?
A: No. It was recorded.

Q: Did the program producer or presenter make a mistake?
A: Yes.

Q: Did they play all of the music they intended to play?
A: Yes.

Q: Was the music on tape or compact disc?
A: No.

4.18 Traffic Trouble

Q: Did the change in traffic regulations mean that more cars passed the area where the sex shops were located?
A: No.

Q: Did the change in regulations cause a change in people's sexual behavior?
A: No.

Q: Did the change in regulations have to do with speeding or parking?
A: No.

Q: Did people buy something from the sex shops which helped them to comply with or evade the new regulations?
A: Yes.

4.19 Blackmail

Q: Did the criminal send an invoice to someone who had not died?
A: No.

Q: Did he send an invoice to someone who was above suspicion of ordering pornographic books?
A: Yes.

Q: Was this because of the dead man's character or profession?
A: No.

4.20 A Good Night's Sleep

Q: Was it a normal hotel?
A: Yes.

Q: Were the drapes normal curtains, used to exclude light at the window?
A: Yes.

Q: Was sound or light stopping him from getting to sleep?
A: No.

Q: Was there something abnormal about the man?
A: Yes.

Q: Was it nighttime?
A: Yes.

Q: Was anyone else involved?
A: No.

4.21 Grateful for Poor Service

Q: Was it a dangerous item which was for sale?
A: No.

Q: Was it a service rather than a product?
A: Yes.

Q: Was there anything about the man which made it wrong or inappropriate for him to use this service?
A: No.

Q: Was the official acting correctly or in the man's best interests?
A: No.

Q: When did this happen?
A: In 1912.

4.22 Free T-shirts

Q: Did ordering and receiving the T-shirt damage his

health in some way?
A: No.

Q: Did it result in financial loss?
A: Yes.

Q: Was the T-shirt offer some kind of scam by criminals?
A: No.

Q: Was the T-shirt offer a genuine offer?
A: No. It had some ulterior purpose.

Q: Was the T-shirt harmless?
A: Yes.

Q: Was the man himself breaking the law?
A: Yes.

Q: Was his name on a wanted list?
A: No.

4.23 Bank Robbery I

Q: Did the bank employee alert the police?
A: Not immediately. He did something more important first.

Q: Did the gang get out of the bank?
A: Yes.

Q: Did they get into their getaway car?
A: No.

Q: Could this have happened in any bank?
A: No.

4.24 Bank Robbery II

Q: Were the robbers frustrated because they could not spend or convert the money they had stolen?
A: Yes.

Q: Did they steal valid currency which could be spent?
A: Yes.

Q: Did they steal numbered or marked notes which could be traced?
A: No.

Q: Could they deposit their loot in other banks?
A: Yes, but that would have given them away.

4.25 A Puzzling Attack

Q: Were any of the four criminals?
A: No.

Q: Did the three have a sound reason for beating up the fourth?
A: Yes. A very sound reason.

Q: Had he said something which inflamed them?
A: Yes.

Q: Were any dwarfs, lighthouse-keepers, or blocks of ice involved?
A: No.

THE ANSWERS

1 Tempting Puzzles

1.1 A Fishy Tale

The vet could see that the goldfish was dying of old age so to spare the old lady's feelings he dashed out and bought a young but identical fish and disposed of the old one.

1.2 The Lost Passenger

Little Billy, as his name suggests, was a goat who unfortunately ate his label, so no one knew where he was supposed to go!

1.3 The Book

She was returning an overdue library book.

1.4 A Hairy Problem

The hair on a man's head is usually at least twenty years older than the hair in his moustache. (This solution is not guaranteed to be biologically correct but it does have an inherent plausibility.)

1.5 The Birds

They were two golfers. In golf parlance, one had hit a "birdie" (one under par) and the other an "eagle" (two under par).

1.6   Blinded at Teatime

He had left his teaspoon in his cup of tea. When he raised the cup to drink, the teaspoon handle poked him in the eye, temporarily blinding him.

1.7   Countdown

The man was counting the pins as he removed them from a new shirt. Unfortunately, he missed one.

1.8   Weather Forecast

In 72 hours it would be midnight again, so it could not be "bright and sunny."

1.9   No West

At the exact center of the earth it is impossible to look east or west but you could look north or south.

1.10   The Blind Beggar

The blind beggar was the sister of her brother who died.

1.11   The Truck Driver

The truck driver was walking.

1.12   Mountains Ahead

The plane is sitting on the ground at the airport in Denver, Colorado.

74

1.13 A Strange Christening

The priest's surplice had caught fire from one of the candles.

1.14 Pond Problem

He lays the planks as shown in this diagram.

1.15 Walking and Running

The two keen sportsmen started at their fitness club, one on the cycling machine and the other on the walking machine. After half an hour of indoor exercise they went for a run. The distance from A to B is 2 miles.

1.16 Church Bells I

The final chime ended abruptly and without the reverberation of the other chimes.

1.17 Church Bells II

There was a joker living in a nearby house. Each night, using his rifle and a silencer, he fired a bullet at the bell after the twelfth stroke.

1.18 A Popular Book

The book is a telephone directory.

1.19 River Problem I

First the man took the duck across, then he came back and took the fox over. He left the fox on the far side of the river and returned with the duck. He then left the duck on the near side and took the corn over. Then he returned and took the duck across. Pretty straightforward, eh?

1.20 River Problem II

The man tied the duck to the back of the boat with a rope. The duck swam along behind the boat as the man ferried the fox and corn over in turn.

1.21 River Problem III

He stretches a long rope from point A to point B as shown.

1.22 Bill and Ben

Bill and Ben are laboratory rats. Bill has run through a certain maze many times and has learned to complete it quickly. When Ben is introduced to the course for the first time, it takes him ten times as long.

1.23 The Missing Brick

A duck grabbed the brick in its mouth and flew off with it!

1.24 A Strange Flight

The duck had a brick in its mouth (see previous puzzle)!

This and the puzzle before it are reciprocal puzzles—each holds the solution to the other.

2 Intriguing Puzzles

2.1 Stamp Collection

The man had recently left his wife to live with his mistress. The angry wife had advertised the man's prized stamp collection for sale, so he quickly bought his own stamps to stop anyone else doing so.

2.2 Sheepish Behavior

The sheep kept coming to the road because they liked to eat the salt put on the road to stop it freezing.

2.3 The Tennis Match

Pete could play tennis with either hand but he was better as a left-hander. He started off playing right-handed but switched after the first set.

2.4 Surrounded

The fugitive leapt up and shouted, "Fire, fire!" Pandemonium broke out and the audience all rushed for the exits. He easily escaped in the confusion.

2.5 The Banker

The train was a roller-coaster. The banker had promised to take his nephew for a ride but hated the experience. He was relieved it was over.

2.6 A Curious Place

The place is Venus, where a day is longer than a year.

Venus takes 225 Earth days to go around the sun but it takes 243 Earth days to rotate on its axis. In any event, it is unlikely that many people would like to go there for either period; the average temperature is around 885°F (460°C), the pressure is about 94 atmospheres, and there are thick clouds of sulphuric acid!

2.7 Grandmother's Letter

The boy's grandmother was Queen Victoria. In this true incident the boy sold the letter for five pounds sterling (over $20 in those days).

2.8 Theft at the Wedding

Two weeks later, when the couple returned from their honeymoon, the whole family sat down to watch the video of the wedding. They were horrified to see, caught on the camera, the groom going through his father-in-law's pockets and stealing his wallet.

2.9 The Free Extension

It is a true story and the man was Picasso. The builder wisely decided that by building the extension he would be able to retain Picasso's rough sketch of the plans, which would be worth far more than the cost of the construction work. He was right.

2.10 Bridge Crossing

They spread out and waded across the river, which was only six inches deep.

2.11 The Seven-Year Itch

The woman had been shipwrecked. She found a pirate's treasure but was not rescued for seven years.

2.12 Hit Out

The patient is a boxer. The last thing he heard was the anesthetist counting 1, 2, 3, 4, and as he comes round he automatically tries to beat the count and resume the fight against his opponent.

2.13 A Green Wedding

The cleric suggested that people throw colored birdseed.

2.14 Sell the Truth

He made the candles that go on birthday cakes.

2.15 The Dried Peas

The dried peas are inside soccer balls for the use of blind people, to enable them to hear the ball.

2.16 The Dog That Did Not Die

This story reportedly concerns the youthful Shirley Temple. Her mother told her the lie that her pet dog had been killed in order to induce real sadness and tears for a movie scene which was about to be filmed.

2.17 High Office

Tom is an infant who is crown prince of his country. Tom's father, the king, has just died leaving a very inexperienced new head of state.

2.18 The Follower

He had seen a man hide in the back of the woman's car as she paid at the gasoline station. He followed her to warn her and was pleased to see her pull into the police station.

2.19 Money to Burn

The robber's mother was a widow who owed the bank $100,000. The bank had threatened to repossess her house so her son devised a plan. He forged $100,000 and she gave it to the bank messenger, who signed for it. The forgeries were good enough to fool the messenger but would never fool the bank so the son had to rob the messenger before he got back to the bank.

2.20 Not a Kidnapper

The inspector noticed that the man wrote with his left hand. He asked him to tie a knot. The man was left-handed and tied a left-handed knot. The knots tied around the hands and feet of the victim were right-handed knots.

2.21 Ruination

The employee discovered an important new product. He left out a primary ingredient in the batch of paper he was making. He was thus responsible for accidentally producing the first blotting paper!

2.22 The Bet

He tied the letter inside a hollowed-out cricket ball (which is about the same size as a baseball). He then had it thrown from man to man with the men standing about 60 yards (55 metres) apart along the entire way.

2.23 Days Off

All seven employees were very religious and they all had different Sabbaths. The Christian took off on Sunday, the Greek Monday, the Persian Tuesday, the Assyrian Wednesday, the Egyptian Thursday, the Arabian Muslim Friday, and the Jew Saturday.

2.24 An Irish Puzzle

Milligan stuffed animals. The man in the garage had heard that Milligan was a famous local taxidermist and thought that he ran some kind of taxi service!

3 Grisly Puzzles

3.1 A Shocking Discovery

He had a pain in his back and when he felt it he found a recently stitched incision. The woman was a lure for a crooked surgeon who removed healthy human organs and sold them to rich people needing organ transplants. On examination by X-ray the man found that one of his kidneys was gone!

3.2 Clean Sweep

The woman works at a teaching hospital as an orderly. It is her job to clean bodies and get them ready for student lectures. She collapses when she sees that the body awaiting her is the body of her brother, who had earlier died in an accident. She did not know that he had left his body to science.

3.3 Death on the Boat

He had been hit by a block of frozen toilet waste ejected by a passenger jet high above him. It fell into the sea leaving no trace.

3.4 A Rum Find

When they finished the rum they broke open the cask to find a body inside. In the eighteenth and nineteenth centuries, bodies were often shipped back to England from Jamaica this way. (British admiral Horatio Nelson's body was reputedly brought home to England in a barrel of rum after the battle of Trafalgar.)

3.5 Broken Match

He and a number of other passengers were making a balloon trip in a desperate attempt to escape from a country. The balloon had to lose weight to stop it from crashing. He drew the short match and had to jump.

3.6 The Cut Finger

This incident took place in South America. The unfortunate man was camping by a river. When he put his hand in the river the blood attracted piranha fish, which removed his finger including the cut!

3.7 The Music Stopped

She was a circus tightrope walker. Her most daring act was to cross a high wire while blindfolded. The band played while she crossed and when the music stopped it was the signal that she had reached the end of the wire and could safely alight. Unfortunately, one day the conductor was taken ill at the last minute and the stand-in conductor, unaware of the importance of the timing, ended the music just a little too soon. She stepped off the wire to her death.

3.8   The Dog Choker

The vet found two human fingers in the dog's throat. They belonged to a burglar. The vet feared that the burglar was still in the house, afraid of the dog and hiding in a closet.

3.9   The Movie

Tom and Joe were the stars of the movie. Tom shot Joe in a sequence in the movie. When Tom left he was mobbed by fans seeking his autograph.

3.10   The Damaged Car

A few minutes earlier, the man had been the driver in a fatal hit-and-run accident. He drove to the isolated area and made it look as though the car had been stolen and vandalized. He then phoned the police to report his car stolen. (This is a true incident. He was later caught and sent to prison.)

3.11   The Motorcyclist

The man was an examiner testing a motorcyclist. He instructed the motorcyclist to go round the block and then to do an emergency stop when the examiner stepped out from the sidewalk. Unfortunately, another motorcyclist of similar appearance came by first. Knowing nothing of the arrangement, he hit the examiner.

3.12   Swimmer in the Forest

During a forest fire some months earlier, a fire-fighting plane had scooped up water from the lake to drop on the fire. The plane had accidentally picked up the unfortunate swimmer.

3.13 The Dark Room

The man was a secret service agent who had recently killed several enemy agents. He entered a confessional in a church and confessed to the killings. However, he was under suspicion and had been followed. The man he confessed to was not a priest but an enemy agent who had seen him enter the church.

3.14 The Two Vans

One man tried to open the front door of his van but could not because of the water pressure. The other man climbed into the back of the van, easily opened the sliding door, and thereby escaped.

3.15 Suicide

The man is a lighthouse-keeper. He woke up in the darkness with a nagging feeling that he had forgotten something. He turned on the radio and heard a report that a ship had crashed onto rocks with great loss of life. He realized that it happened because he forgot to start the light that night.

3.16 The Plane Crash

The movie had been shown a week earlier. Susan had taped it then on her videocassette recorder to watch that evening.

3.17 One Beautiful Morning

The man was the leader of a religious cult. Believing that the world would end that night he had offered his followers the choice of taking poison or seeing the destruction of the world. Many, including his own children, had chosen poison. He and others had gone to sleep expecting to wake to Armageddon. When the next day dawned as a beautiful summer morning he knew that he had made a terrible mistake.

3.18   The Blanket Mystery

He was an Indian brave who sent smoke signals alerting a war party to the approach of a cavalry troop.

3.19   The Deadly Bite

The woman was Eve, who gave Adam the forbidden fruit from the tree in the Garden of Eden. By breaking God's instruction, Adam became mortal and died.

3.20   The Bad Boy

Out of mischief, the boy climbed onto the roof of the man's house and placed a plank of wood over the chimney. The man, who had been asleep in his parlor, was suffocated by fumes from his fire.

4 Diabolical Puzzles

4.1   The Nursery Rhyme

The man recites the nursery rhyme "This little piggy went to market, this little piggy stayed home . . ." while wiggling each of the baby's toes. But there is one toe too many! To his embarrassment, he finds that the baby has six toes on one foot.

4.2   The Elder Twin

At the time she went into labor, the twins' mother was travelling from Guam to Hawaii. The older twin, Terry, was born on March 1st. Shortly afterwards, the mother crossed the International Date Line and Kerry, the younger twin, was born. The date was February 28th. In leap years, the younger twin celebrates her birthday two days before the older twin, since February 28 is two days before March 1st.

4.3   Fair Shares

Suppose there are a number of people. Pick one person, A, by lot if necessary. Ask A to cut a piece of the cake that he would be happy with as his share. Now go round the group. If B objects then ask B to cut a bit off A's piece so that he (B) would be happy to take what remains. If B does not object ask C and so on. If nobody objects, then let A have that piece. Continuing this process will give a division which satisfies everybody.

4.4   The Sealed Envelope

There is usually a small gap at the top of the envelope where the flap has been folded over. The wife inserted a knitting needle through the gap and under the fold of the letter. By rotating the needle she wound the letter tightly around it. She then removed it, read the letter, and replaced it using the actions in reverse.

4.5   Tattoo

The men were sailors, who were often flogged for minor offenses on board ship. Some captains refused to whip a man's back if it carried the image of Christ.

4.6   Suitcase for Hire

Pat was a Westerner in Tokyo. Houses there are small and, in order to save space, people tend to rent any large item which they might use only occasionally. Most Japanese rent the suitcases they take on holiday.

4.7   The Tennis Tournament

The answer is 212 matches including the final. There is a very easy way to solve this seemingly difficult problem. Each match must produce one winner and one loser. Everyone except the tournament winner loses exactly once, so the number of matches is exactly the same as the number of losers. So to have 212 losers there must be exactly 212 matches.

4.8   The Key

The man's wife was an habitual sleepwalker. She had previously opened the front door in her sleep and walked out
into the road. He placed the key in the bucket of cold
water so that, if she reached into the water to get it, the
cold sensation would waken her.

4.9   That's Fast!

Harry broke a pane of glass. A crack in glass starts in one
place and travels across the glass at a speed of over 3000
miles (4800 kilometres) per hour.

4.10   A Man in a Bar

The man was a priest conducting a communion service in
a nearby church when they ran short of altar wine. Only
red wine would do.

4.11   The 88 Hours

The man had a nasty toothache and he went to the dentist
at 5 P.M. on a Friday evening. The dentist's assistants,
including the anesthetist, had all gone and the dentist
could not administer an anesthetic. The man insisted that
the dentist should operate even without anesthetic so the
dentist said that he would have to strap the man into the
chair. This was done. The dentist then suffered a heart
attack and died. The poor man was left strapped in the
chair and unable to move. It was a holiday weekend and
no staff reported for work until 9 A.M. on the following
Tuesday morning—88 hours later.

4.12   Sand Trap

This incident reputedly occurred during the war between
Israel and Egypt. Because of import duties, Mercedes cars

were much more expensive in Egypt than in Israel. When Israel seized vast tracts of the Sinai desert, a clever Israeli businessman realized that the land would have to be handed back to Egypt after the war. By burying the cars he effectively exported them when the border shifted without them actually moving! His Egyptian associate subsequently sold them at a handsome profit.

4.13   Building Demolition

The building was the Australian National Mint. Over many years, so much gold dust had been absorbed into the fabric of the building that it was well worthwhile to demolish the building, extract the gold, and rebuild.

4.14   The Torn Cheque

The man had ordered a bicycle for his son as a gift. The advertisement had not stated that it came in 217 pieces as a self-assembly kit. This was his revenge.

4.15   The Weather Report

Since the weather report did not specify degrees in Fahrenheit or Celsius/centigrade, the temperature must have been the same in both scales. Only a temperature of -40 degrees is the same in both Fahrenheit and Celsius/centigrade. That temperature for June would certainly make the place Antarctica.

4.16   Odd Animals

They are all impostors:
The koala bear is not a bear; it is a marsupial.
The prairie dog is not a dog; it is a rodent.
The firefly is not a fly; it is a beetle.

90

The silkworm is not a worm; it is a caterpillar.
The jackrabbit is not a rabbit; it is a hare.
The guinea pig is not a pig; it is a rodent (and it is not from Guinea, but from South America).

4.17 The Shorter Program

It was a program of contemporary classical music played from a record. The record was played at the wrong speed—45 rpm instead of 33 rpm. Because of the esoteric nature of the composition, this mistake was not noticed until the end of the transmission. It can easily be calculated that the program should have lasted thirty minutes.

4.18 Traffic Trouble

A new traffic regulation, designed to encourage car sharing, stated that only cars carrying two or more passengers could use certain lanes of the freeway. This led to motorists buying blow-up dolls to give the appearance that they were carrying passengers!

4.19 Blackmail

The criminal sent an invoice to a blind man who had recently died. His widow immediately knew that it must be a scam.

4.20 A Good Night's Sleep

The man was deaf. He had to get up early for an important meeting and he was so worried about oversleeping that he could not get to sleep. After opening the curtains, however, he knew that the sunlight would wake him up, so he was no longer worried and fell asleep easily.

4.21 Grateful for Poor Service

The man wanted to buy a first-class ticket on the maiden voyage of the luxury liner *Titanic* in 1912. He was refused because he was black. The *Titanic* sank with great loss of life.

4.22 Free T-shirts

This is a true story from Connecticut. The advertisement was a trap for people who used illegal devices to tap into cable television circuits without paying. It was placed by the owners of the cable television network and could be seen only by people using illegal decoders.The "free" T-shirt was soon followed by a letter informing them that they were committing a federal crime and imposing a $2000 fine. The recipients had little choice but to pay up.

4.23 Bank Robbery I

The bank was on the sixth floor of a tall building. The staff member who struggled free pressed a security button which froze all the elevators. The gang was trapped inside the elevator until the police came to arrest them.

4.24 Bank Robbery II

The robbers discovered to their horror that the currency consisted only of freshly minted coins. All shops and banks were alerted to watch out for anyone trying to exchange large amounts of coin, so the gang was reduced to playing slot machines!

4.25 A Puzzling Attack

They had been trying to solve a lateral thinking problem—this one in fact. When the one posing the problem revealed the answer the others beat him up. (In setting this puzzle, always describe the group and the problem poser in terms of the number of men and women in your own group.)

About the Authors

Paul Sloane was born in Scotland and grew up near Blackpool in the north of England. He studied engineering at Trinity Hall, Cambridge, and graduated with a first-class honors degree. While at Cambridge he met his wife, who is a teacher. They live in Camberley, England, with their three daughters.

Most of Paul Sloane's career has been in the computer industry and he is currently the European vice-president for a software company. He has always been an avid collector and creator of puzzles. His first book, *Lateral Thinking Puzzlers*, was published by Sterling in 1991. Paul Sloane has given speeches and radio talks on the topic of change management and lateral thinking.

Des MacHale was born in County Mayo, Ireland, and is Associate Professor of Mathematics at University College in Cork. He was educated at University College, Galway, and the University of Keele in England. He and his wife, Anne, have five children.

The author of over thirty books, mostly of humor but also one on giving up smoking, Des MacHale has many interests including puzzles, geology, writing, broadcasting, films, photography, numismatics, and, of course, mathematics. He is currently working on three more books.

This is the second book co-authored by Paul Sloane and Des MacHale. It follows on the success of their first book, *Challenging Lateral Thinking Puzzles*, also published by Sterling.

INDEX

Page key: **puzzle**, *clue*, solution